Abū Zayd al-Balkhī's
SUSTENANCE OF THE SOUL
THE COGNITIVE BEHAVIOR THERAPY OF A NINTH CENTURY PHYSICIAN

*Translation and annotation of the
ninth century manuscript by*

Malik Badri

THE INTERNATIONAL INSTITUTE OF ISLAMIC THOUGHT
LONDON · WASHINGTON

REPRINTED 1439AH/2018CE
6TH REPRINT 1444AH/2022CE

P.O. BOX 669, HERNDON, VA 20172, USA
www.iiit.org

LONDON OFFICE
P.O. BOX 126, RICHMOND, SURREY TW9 2UD, UK
www.iiituk.com

978-1-56564-599-8

Layout and Design by Shiraz Khan
Printed in the USA

Foreword

Lying preserved in the Ayasofya Library in Istanbul, Turkey is an astonishing manuscript. Written in two distinct parts, forming two separate works, it is by the well-known ninth century CE polymath, Abū Zayd Aḥmad ibn Sahl al-Balkhī, entitled *Maṣāliḥ al-Abdān wa al-Anfus* (Sustenance for Bodies and Souls). Famous for his contributions to geography and literature, this was Abū Zayd al-Balkhī's only manuscript on psychological medicine.

Centuries ahead of his time in realizing the importance of both mental, as well as physical, health for human wellbeing, al-Balkhī discusses some very modern ideas, in a rather modern, self-help style manual. A creative genius his insights on human psychopathology as well as diagnoses of psychological ailments including stress, depression, fear and anxiety, phobic and obsessive-compulsive disorders, together with their treatment by cognitive behavior therapy, relate to us in every way and are in sync with modern psychology. They also incorporate a greater dimension to include the soul and most importantly the worship of God.

Al-Balkhī explains symptoms and treatments giving advice on preventive measures and how to return the body and soul to their natural healthy state. In doing so he displays a keen understanding of the human condition and the medical nature of the human emotional state.

This work is an English translation of the second part of al-Balkhī's manuscript (Sustenance of the Soul), possibly of greater interest to readers given the world-wide increase in mental and psychological disorders including stress, anxiety and depression. And although anxiety and mood disorders sound commonplace to us today, it must be remembered that al-Balkhī lived more than eleven centuries ago in fact, and that these disorders were largely left undiagnosed for centuries before being studied and clinically defined as such, and only as relatively recently as the late 19th century. Note that Robert Burton's *The Anatomy of Melancholy*, a rather diversionary work of somewhat questionable medical strength, was published only in the 17th century and focused largely only on that particular condition.

Al-Balkhī's advanced understanding anticipating so long ago what we know to be true today speaks volumes for the brilliance of the man whose works should be read and whose legacy should not lie forgotten.

The IIIT, established in 1981, has served as a major center to facilitate serious scholarly efforts based on Islamic vision, values and principles. The Institute's programs of research, seminars and conferences during the last thirty years have resulted in the publication of more than four hundred titles in English and Arabic, many of which have been translated into other major languages. We thank the editorial team at the IIIT London Office, including Shiraz Khan, and all those involved with the production of this work.

IIIT London Office
July 2013

ACKNOWLEDGEMENT

Firstly, I would like to express my gratitude to renowned Iranian Professor, M. Muhaqqiq, for drawing my attention to Fuat Sezgin's reproduction of al-Balkhī's manuscript, *Maṣāliḥ al-Abdān wa al-Anfus* (Sustenance for Bodies and Souls). This was in the early 1990s when we were both professors at the International Institute of Islamic Thought and Civilization (ISTAC), Kuala Lumpur. Being professor of philosophy and Islamic studies with special interest in the works of early Muslim scholars, M. Muhaqqiq came across the manuscript and informed me of it due to my interest in the history of psychology. It was an appreciable gift as my early writings on the text were quickly quoted by Arab and Muslim psychologists. One of these scholars and a close friend, Professor Abbas Hussain, was the first to venture an English translation of the work. However his work was interrupted when he resigned from his post at the International Islamic University to join a Saudi company. Nevertheless, in recognition of al-Balkhī's incomparable contributions contained in the manuscript, the Institute requested I teach it as a trimester course to its postgraduate students.

I am also indebted to my dear friend, Professor Mustafa Ashwi, for his insistent request that we cooperate in writing a psycho-historical treatise on the manuscript in Arabic. To this end he wrote a long historical and bio-graphical introduction, as well as summarizing and authenticating the whole manuscript from a historical and psychological point of view. I discussed al-Balkhī's contributions from a psychotherapeutic and psychiatric perspective. The book had the same title as the manuscript and was published in Arabic by King Faisal Research Centre in Riyadh. Without doubt such a useful publication would not have been accomplished without Professor Ashwi's untiring enthusiasm.

Lastly, my gratitude and appreciation are respectfully extended to two universities. Firstly, the International Islamic University in Malaysia and particularly its Research and Publications Centre at the International Institute of Islamic Thought and Civilization headed at the time by my dear friend, Professor Sayyid Ajmal al-Aidrus. Like Professor Ashwi, Ajmal pressured me into writing the present translation of the manuscript. I am also thankful to him and to Professor Hassan Alnagar for editing my translation. In extending my gratitude to the International Islamic University, I would also like to record my thankfulness to Professor Kamal Hassan, the previous Rector and one of the founders of the University. I humbly appreciate his blessed encouragement and his brotherly support.

Secondly, the Ahfad University for Women in Sudan, and particularly its President, Professor Gasim Badri, who offered me the post of research professor providing me with all the facilities necessary to write the books and articles that otherwise I had no time to complete whilst a busy professor and psychotherapist at the International Islamic University in Malaysia. Completing the translation of Balkhī's manuscript and writing its introductory sections is the first production of this research professorship.

Malik Badri

Omdurman, Sudan • 12 JUNE 2012

Abū Zayd al-Balkhī's

· SUSTENANCE OF THE SOUL ·

Who was Abū Zayd al-Balkhī?

ABŪ ZAYD AL-BALKHĪ was an encyclopedic genius whose profound contributions to knowledge covered many diverse fields that would seem, to our modern minds, to be unrelated to each other. He is also considered to be one of the world's first known cognitive psychologists, astonishingly centuries ahead of his time, studying and suggesting cognitive treatments to anxiety and mood disorders.

A polymath and prolific writer, he authored more than sixty books and manuscripts, meticulously researching disciplines as varied in scope as geography, medicine, theology, politics, philosophy, poetry, literature, Arabic grammar, astrology, astronomy, mathematics, biography, ethics, sociology as well as others. Although excelling in many fields his fame as a great scholar came actually as a result of his work in geography leading him to become the founder of what is known as the "Balkhī School" of terrestrial mapping. Regrettably, most of these valuable documents, hand-written manuscripts, have either been lost or lie concealed in museums or in inaccessible libraries.

Similarly, very little has been written by way of biography. Most of what we know about al-Balkhī comes from a single biographer, Yāqūt al-Ḥamawī. In a well-known volume on the biographies of poets and men of letters, *Muʿjam al-Udabāʾ*, al-Ḥamawī states that al-Balkhī's full name was Abū Zayd Aḥmad ibn Sahl al-Balkhī, and that he was born in the year 235 AH (849 CE) in a small village called Shamisitiyan, in the Persian province of Balkh, which is now part of Afghanistan. Aside from noting that he received his early education from his father, Ḥamawī does not mention any other information about al-Balkhī's childhood. He does however, provide some detailed information on his youth and endeavors to educate himself in the sciences and arts of his time.

Al-Ḥamawī chronicles that one of al-Balkhī's students, Abū Muḥammad al-Ḥassan ibn al-Wazīrī, described him to be a slim man of medium height, deep brown complexion and protruding eyes, with a face bearing the marks of smallpox. He was generally silent, and contemplative thus exhibiting a (reserved) shy personality. This description of his personality added to the meticulous nature of his vast and rigorously written studies in modern terminology, allows us to infer al-Balkhī to be a highly introverted, yet brilliant scholar. What also seems apparent is that he preferred seclusion and contemplation to socializing with friends or attending parties because there is no mention in his biography of either, whether association with intimate friends or attendance of lavish parties, by lavish meaning eating, listening to music and/or captivating Arabic poetry, common in the Abbasid era. This conclusion is strongly supported the more we read al-Ḥamawī's account of him.

If al-Balkhī had mixed in social circles as early Muslim physicians such as Abū al-Faraj ibn Hindū and Abū Bakr al-Rāzī, had done we would have known more about his personal life, and more about the fate of his missing, great contributions. For example, we know that Ibn Hindū's treatise, *Miftāḥ al-Ṭibb wa Minhāj al-Ṭullāb* (The Key to Medicine and the Students' Guide) one of the greatest contributions to medicine of the 11th century, was the product of a request made by friends. In his introduction to this inimitable treatise, Ibn Hindū states:

> Some of my learned friends have looked through my book entitled, *A Treatise Encouraging the Study of Philosophy*; its easily understood style made them want a similar treatise on medicine. So I undertook to compose such a treatise for them, taking pains to make it accessible, and called it 'The Key to Medicine'.

So, it was Ibn Hindū's sociability and reverence for friendship that enabled the legacy of this priceless historical document to be left to us.

Similarly, it was fascination with music and musical parties that led al-Rāzī to one of his greatest medical inventions. Al-Rāzī was a famous musician before becoming one of the most distinguished physicians of all time. Yet, his great medical successes did not weaken his love for music and he would invite musicians to his house to play in the evenings with instruments such as violins and lutes, the strings of which were made from animal intestines. At one of these parties, his guests stayed far into the night, and too tired to carry their instruments back left them in al-Rāzī's care. Now al-Rāzī kept a few domesticated monkeys in the house for medical research and one of these cut the strings off the instruments and ate them. Al-Rāzī decided to use the incident for a scientific experiment. Keeping the monkey under close observation, he examined its faeces for remains of the strings. Nothing appeared and he realized that the strings had been fully digested. This resulted in one of medicine's greatest inventions, the use of dissolving catgut strings to stitch wounds (al-Fanjārī, pp. 81-82).

Although some historians of Islamic medicine credit al-Zahrāwī with the invention of dissolving sutures, it was in fact al-Rāzī, as both a musician and a physician, who made this great discovery. The point being that science sometimes finds its inspiration in creativity, and also, as in this case and that of Ibn Hindū, by way of simple sociability.

We should also be grateful for al-Balkhī's introspective and intro-verted personality, in that it was this and its concomitant traits that bestowed on him the patience and astute clinical acuity, to write *Maṣāliḥ al-Abdān wa al-Anfus*. Without introspective, analytical thought, and penetrative clinical perception al-Balkī would not, in the 9th century, have been able to write in such detail about psychoso-matic disorders, to be able to differentiate between psychoses and neuroses, to categorize depression as normal, reactive and endoge-nous, or to give a detailed exposition on the use of cognitive therapy in treating psychological disorders. As he rightly asserts in his manu-script, no scholar before him had written a medical treatise of this kind.

As mentioned earlier, al-Balkhī was not only a great physician but also a polymath, an eminent geographer, and a great Muslim theolo-gian. He was also a master of Arabic prose and not argumentative. In describing his eloquence al-Wazīrī, as quoted by al-Ḥamawī, states that when al-Balkhī spoke it was as if "a shower of gems" had fallen. He was unsurpassed in expression. Al-Wazīrī compares him with al-Jāḥiz and ʿAlī ibn ʿUbaydah al-Rayḥānī, the two most prominent writers of his time, and quotes the linguists of the time stating that al-Balkhī was more articulate than both since his words were more eloquent and he was able to elucidate any topic with ease, whereas in comparison al-Jāḥiẓ was verbose and al-Rayḥānī, too laconic.

In describing Balkhī's style of writing, al-Ḥamawī notes that his great knowledge of classical and modern sciences gave to his written work the style of philosophers, and the eloquence of men of letters. Some of his writings have indeed become wise sayings and proverbs. For example:

> If someone praises you for what is not in you, then you cannot trust that he will not blame you for what is not in you.
> Religion is the greatest of philosophies; therefore, man cannot be a philosopher until he becomes a worshipper.
> The greatest medicine is knowledge.

Al-Balkhī did not earn this prestigious scholarly status without humbly enduring the hardships of patient learning. Al-Ḥamawī notes that he traveled from Balkh, his home town, to Baghdad to reside there for eight long years in search of religious and secular knowledge, and to acquire the scholarly methodology of his time. Among his great teachers was the renowned philosopher, Abū Yūsuf al-Kindī.

According to al-Ḥamawī during this period al-Balkhī became deeply engrossed in conflicting philosophical issues that confounded his religious beliefs and caused him to divert from the right path of Sunni Islam. This led some religious Muslim scholars to accuse him of deviance. So much so in fact that at one time, he was considered an adherent of the Shiʿism of al-Imāmiyyah or al-Zaydiyyah and at other times, an adherent of the Muʿtazilah school of thought. This confirms our conjecture of al-Balkhī being a young, lonely, reflective introvert, without intimate friends who at the time could have helped him out of his spiritual crisis.

It was a turbulent era in any case, the Abbasid caliphate had lost much of its powerful grip over its people, resulting in theological upheaval, and the rise of destructive movements such as al-Qarāmiṭah and what has come to be known as the negro revolutionary movement c. 868 CE which almost brought about the caliphate's downfall.

4

However, this youthful state of confusion did not last long. Al-Ḥamawī asserts that after Baghdad's culture shock, al-Balkhī finally established himself on the right path of the Sunni School, as apparent in his work *Kitāb Naẓm al-Qurʾān*, which exceeded all that had been written in this field. Furthermore, unlike the Shia he was annoyed by those who gave preference to some of the companions of the Prophet (ṢAAS)* over others, and detested the pomposity of Arabs over non-Arabs.

After completing his studies in Baghdad, al-Balkhī returned to Balkh and there took up the post of *kātib* (literally writer) or secretary to Prince Aḥmad ibn Sahl ibn Hāshim al-Marwazī, the ruler of Balkh and its suburbs. In fact the ruler offered him a ministerial as well as a writing position. However, al-Balkhī turned down the former and accepted the latter. The ruler respected his choice and paid him well.

Again, al-Balkhī's choice confirms our belief as to his unsociable nature. Limiting himself to the role of *kātib* allowed al-Balkhī more time for reclusive in-depth study, and it was perhaps due to this personality trait that he avoided the more prestigious, but socially demanding job of minister. Al-Balkhī continued to research and write until the age of eighty-eight, avoiding the temptations of jobs of better status and higher salary.

In relation to this, al-Ḥamawī narrates that the king of Khurāsān himself invited al-Balkhī to assist him in his kingdom, but he politely declined. He visited Baghdad for a second time, but quickly returned to Balkh and lived there until his death in the year 934 CE.

The subject of this book is al-Balkhī's ninth century manuscript *Maṣāliḥ al-Abdān wa al-Anfus* (Sustenance for Bodies and Souls), comprised of 361 pages and located in the Ayasofya Library, Istanbul. Written in clear, easy to read Arabic, the hand written document (no. 3741) consists of 268 pages devoted to the sustenance of the body and 73 pages to the sustenance of the soul or psyche.

Our translation is limited to the second psychotherapeutic part, concerning the sustenance of the soul. As expected, the first part on the

---

* *Ṣallā Allāhu ʿalayhi wa sallam*. May the peace and blessings of God be upon him. Said whenever the name of Prophet Muhammad is mentioned.

sustenance of the body deals with the physical aspects of health. In writing this section, al-Balkhī naturally developed it from the outdated medical knowledge of the 9th century which had been greatly influenced by the theories and practices of Greek physicians. Much of what he has included in this part would be of great interest to historians of medicine.

However, what is worth noting is that even in writing this part, al-Balkhī, a great scholar of psychosomatic medicine, has surprisingly discussed medical and psychosomatic issues of interest to modern medical practitioners. The sustenance of the physical health of man is discussed in 14 chapters, with the approach being largely preventative, to preserve health, and protect the body from physical disorders. With tremendous foresight he includes two chapters on environmental and public health: the first on the importance of having a suitable house, pure water and clean air, and the second on protecting the body by avoiding the extremes of hot and cold temperatures, and by wearing proper clothing. Other chapters include the importance of nutrition, that is proper nourishment with suitable food and drink, good sleep and cleanliness of the body.

Al-Balkhī also recognized the importance of physical exercise and massage, comparing bodily fluids to nature's stagnant and running water, noting that just as stagnant water quickly becomes polluted and unhygienic whilst running water preserves its purity, likewise lack of physical exercise can cause body humors to become stagnant and eventually pathological.

Some of the chapters in this section do not fall wholly into either category of physical or psychological ailments, but discuss psychophysical issues related to music therapy and aromatherapy, i.e. there is a chapter on the benefits of music and perfume in relaxing the body and treating physical ailments.

Finally, in the ninth chapter of the treatise al-Balkhī introduces an extremely delicate subject, one remarkably ahead of its time which today would be the domain of modern sex therapists, and this is the study of various sexual attributes and their affects. Thus, he considers sexual abstinence to be unnatural and a cause for certain physical problems, and wet dreams a mechanism employed by the body to get rid of 'trapped' potentially harmful ejaculates. He even suggests methods for the treatment of sexual impotence including certain foods and drink and notes the harmful effects on the body of medications that at the time purported to improve sexuality.

Following this brief summary of Balkhī and his work *Sustenance for Bodies*, we turn next to an introduction by distinguished Turkish scholar, Fuat Sezgin, the first to discover the priceless value of the manuscript and have it published by the Institute of the History of the Arab Islamic Sciences (Germany), of which he is the founder and honorary director. He is also professor emeritus of the History of Natural Science at Johann Wolfgang Goethe University in Frankfurt.

REFERENCES

Badri, M. B. and Ashwi, M., *Maṣāliḥ al-Abdān wa al-Anfus: A Psychologist who Needed 10 Centuries to be Appreciated.* (Riyadh: King Faisal Research Center, 1424 AH).

Abū Zayd al-Balkhī, *Maṣāliḥ al-Abdān wa al-Anfus*, [Sustenance for Bodies and Souls]. (Frankfurt: Institute for the History of Arabic-Islamic Science, 1984).

Al-Fanjārī, A., Islamic Sciences, (in Arabic). (Kuwait: The Kuwaiti Institute of the Advancement of Science, 1958).

Al-Ḥamawī, Yāqūt, *Mu'jam Al'udaba'*. (Beirut: Dār al-Fikr Publications, 1980).

Ibn Hindū, Abū al-Faraj, *The Key to Medicine and the Students' Guide.* Translated by Aida Tibi. (Doha: The Center for Muslim Contribution, 2010).

Introduction

FUAT SEZGIN

Institute of the History of the Arab-Islamic Sciences
Frankfurt, Germany • November, 1984

Abū Zayd Aḥmad ibn Sahl al-Balkhī (236–322/
850–934), the author of the book here presented, was one of
the greatest scholars of his time. In the fields of philosophy,
mathematics, history, geography, medicine, belles lettres, grammar,
and others, he composed about sixty works, most of them non-exis-
tent.[1] From the few which have survived, however, we gather that Abū
Zayd was a natural philosopher possessed of a vast fund of knowledge,
a capacity for original thinking, and a concise literary style.[2]

The *Maṣāliḥ al-Abdān wa al-Anfus* is perhaps Abū Zayd's only
contribution in the field of medicine. It seeks the preservation of health
in the human, by giving simultaneous and comprehensive attention to
both, body and soul together with the diseases to which they are
subject.

As he himself put it, "The right approach is to supplement minis-
trations to the body with those directed to the soul; this is essential."
The benefit is intensified by reason of the interrelation between the
two. Man's constitution is from both his soul and body; there is no con-
ceiving that he may endure, except by their union, giving rise to human
actions. The two participate in events, both joyful and sorrowful, and
in accidental pain.

---

[1] Cf. Sezgin, *Geschichte Des Arabischen Schrifttums*, vol. 3, p. 274; vol. 6, pp. 190-
191; vol. 9, p. 189.

[2] His terse style attracted the attention of Arabic authors after his time: "There is
unanimous world agreement among the literati that in this there are three pre-eminent
stylists: Al-Jāḥiẓ, ʿAlī ibn ʿUbaydah, and Abū Zayd al-Balkhī. Among those the flow of
whose words exceeds their meaning is al-Jāḥiẓ; the one whose meanings exceed the
words is ʿAlī ibn ʿUbaydah, but with Abū Zayd his meanings are matched by his words"
(Yāqūt, *Irshād al-Arīb*, London edition, vol. 1, p. 148).

Abū Zayd al-Balkhī

Thus when the body is undergoing illness and pain, and when stricken by harmful symptoms, these also hamper the strength of the soul "conversely, the onset of mental pain leads to corporeal diseases" (p. 272 273).

This remark lead him to the composition of the book's second treatise, where he deems himself the first to devote, to this theme, an independent study. At the same time he indicates the amount of gratitude and appreciation due to his ancestors because of their indirect contributions, "in diverse places among the books of the learned, and the people devoted to wisdom and enlightenment" (p. 274).

Perhaps we are not mistaken in regarding this second treatise of Abū Zayd al-Balkhī, the first attempt to collect the various topics of the branch of medicine which treats mental diseases, together with psychosomatic and psychotherapeutic treatment.

Concerning the final decision as to him being the pioneer of psychopathological medicine, this is left to the specialists in the field.

The outstanding and independent personality of Abū Zayd is apparent also from the first treatise of his book, devoted to the well being of the body, the standard subject dealt with in the medical literature since antiquity.

We lay special emphasis upon the significance of opinions and information given by the author in the first treatise concerning human geography, meteorological phenomena, and environmental science, when relevant to the topic being discussed.

Two copies of the work are preserved in the Ayasofya Library, Istanbul. The first of them, which we are reproducing here with the kind permission of the Turkish authorities, is MS 3741, copied in 884 AH/1479 AD. The second, MS 3740, was also copied in the ninth century of the Hijra, and comprises 140 folios. It is my duty to mention with appreciation and thanks the collaboration of our Institute staff in the publication of this book.

Publication of the Institute of the History of the Arab-Islamic Sciences
Frankfurt, Germany • Series C-Volume 2, pp. 362–63

Sustenance of the Soul
[Part 2 of Maṣāliḥ al-Abdān wa al-Anfus]

THE MANUSCRIPT IN BRIEF:
A SUMMARY BY THE TRANSLATOR

Abū Zayd al-Balkhī
A ninth century genius of psychological medicine

In his masterpiece on the *Sustenance of the Soul*, Abū Zayd al-Balkhī presented physicians of the ninth century with medical and psychotherapeutic information that was far ahead of his time and only discovered or developed more than eleven centuries after his death. He was probably the first physician to clearly differentiate between mental and psychological disorders; between psychoses and neuroses. He was also the first to classify emotional disorders in a strikingly modern way and to categorize them in one general classification. His nosology classifies neuroses into four types: Fear and panic (*al-khawf wa al-fazaʿ*); anger and aggression (*al-ghaḍab*); sadness and depression (*al-ḥuzn wa al-jazaʿ*); and obsessions (*al-waswasah*). Furthermore, he wrote in great detail of how rational and spiritual cognitive therapy could be used to treat each one of his classified disorders.

The titles of his eight chapters on the sustenance of the soul, resemble the table of contents of a modern text on cognitive psychotherapy and mental hygiene. He writes in the most eloquent Arabic style to clearly differentiate between the normal and extreme emotional reactions of normal people, and those whose emotionality has already become pathological. His approach is both preventive and therapeutic underscored by an amazing psychophysiological approach.

The first chapter is composed of an introductory article discussing the importance of sustaining the health of the *nafs* or soul, a synonym to the modern conception of the psyche or mind, but with an Islamic spiritual dimension. Chapter two entitled "Sustenance of Psychological

Health" comprises an ultra modern essay on mental hygiene or preventive mental health. Chapter three is titled "Ways of Regaining Psychological Health When One Loses It." The title of Chapter four is, "Enumerating the Psychological Symptoms and Specifying their Distinguishing Attributes," being the exact translation of the Arabic title, *Dhikr al-Aʿrādh al-Nafsāniyyah wa Taʿdīdihā*. The Arabic word *aʿrādh* is the plural of *ʿaradh* which is used in modern medicine and psychiatry to stand for the English word 'symptom'. Al-Balkhī however uses the term *aʿrādh* for both symptoms and disorders. So his usage of the terms *al-Aʿrādh al-Nafsāniyyah* in the title of the chapter actually means "psychological disorders." The title of Chapter five is, "How to Counteract Anger and Get Rid of It;" Chapter six, "Tranquillizing Fear," (*Taskīn al-Khawf wa al-Fazaʿ*); Chapter seven, "Methods of Dealing with Sadness and Depression," (*Tadbīr Dafʿ al-Ḥuzn wa al-Jazaʿ*); and lastly Chapter eight is on "Mental Maneuvers that Fend off the Recurring Whispers of the Heart and the Obsessive Inner Speech of the Soul," (*Fī al-Iḥtiyāl li Dafʿ Wasāwis al-Ṣadr wa Aḥādīth al- Nafs*).

Al-Balkhī's timeless contribution is undoubtedly to the fields of cognitive and behavior therapy and psychosomatic medicine. I will do my best to simplify this summary so that lay readers, whether in psychiatry and clinical psychology or not, can appreciate the contributions of this genius.

Al-Balkhī: A Pioneer of Psychosomatic Medicine

On reading the translation of the manuscript, what becomes clear is that al-Balkhī continuously compares physical with psychological disorders, illustrating beautifully how they interact with each other to form psychosomatic disorders. Another fascinating contribution is his highlighting of the importance of individual differences in the development and treatment of emotional and psychosomatic disorders. In discussing these aspects (p.270–71), he begins the manuscript by stating that since man is composed of a body and a soul, he must have from each of them a condition of health or sickness, balance or imbalance.

Disorders of the body are like fever, headache and other physical illnesses; that of the soul are like anger, anxiety, sadness and other similar symptoms.

He criticizes the medical practitioners of his time for their infatuation with physical illnesses and symptoms and their restriction of therapy to physical means such as medicines and bloodletting (p.272). He states that they neglected psychological aspects to the extent that their books were devoid of any reference or material on the sustenance of the *nafs* or soul and its psychological aspects.

He thus believed his book to be unique in that it combined the sustenance of the body with that of the soul in one volume, forming thereby an unprecedented contribution. He strongly asserts that he knew of no person before him who had written on the sustenance of the soul and its relation to the body in the clear simplified way that he had done. He emphasizes his approach was very much needed by patients because of the intimate interaction of the body and mind. He uses the Arabic word *ishtibāk* for this psychosomatic interaction which literally means intertwining, interweaving or entangling, in itself indicating his refined understanding of the phenomenon.

Al-Balkhī's criticism of the ninth century physicians of his time is remarkably applicable to most contemporary doctors of our time. In his best-selling book, *Timeless Healing*, Hebert Benson reiterates the same criticism when writing that doctors,

> get used to seeing symptoms and signs of illness and injury separate from actual patients…Doctors often take these habits with them into medical practice, emphasizing specifics over wholeness, body over mind, leaving many patients underwhelmed by their compassion or interest. (pp.248-249)

Al-Balkhī defends his psychosomatic position by asserting that human existence itself cannot be imagined without this *ishtibāk* or interaction. He notes that if a body becomes sick, the *nafs* or soul or self would lose much of its cognitive and comprehensive abilities and fail to enjoy the pleasurable aspects of life. On the other hand, if the soul becomes sick, the body may find no joy in life and may eventually develop a physical illness. He goes on to strongly stress that helping people with their psychological symptoms is accordingly highly essential not only because of this psychosomatic interaction, but also because they are more common than physical symptoms. A person may live for years, he asserts, without complaining from any physical symptoms, but psychological symptoms plague us all the time (p.270 71).

Although al-Balkhī emphasizes the importance of emotional stress and disorders in giving rise to psychological illness that may cause the body to react pathologically, he nevertheless does not forget the existence of individual differences between people in interpreting the stress and reacting to it. He notes that although the level of emotional stress facing different persons may be of the same strength, their symptomatic responses to life's problems may be quite varied. Some are hot tempered, some are slow to get angry, some may panic faced with a terrifying situation, whilst others may have the ability to stay calm. There also exist individual differences between men and woman and children (p.271).

Al-Balkhī as a Modern Counseling Psychologist

One of al-Balkhī's greatest merits, as will become apparent when reading the translation, is that in spite of dealing with neurotics and emotionally disordered persons, his work is not limited to such "patients". He also covers the emotional abnormality of normal persons. Furthermore, he does not speak of a so-called neurotic as a "patient" but rather as a person whose emotional overreactions have become a habit. This humane approach stresses that emotional disorder is simply a learned habit that need not divide people into normal persons and patients. It is a much needed approach in modern psychotherapy which, because it has adopted a medical model, has largely limited itself to a therapeutic endeavor for the sick and not as a form of psychological healing for those who are simply unhappy.

It is of interest to note that contemporary therapists are only just beginning to adopt what al-Balkhī in fact emphasized more than eleven centuries ago! Many modern psychologists and psychiatrists are now critiquing this paradigmatic dilemma, and questioning the Freudian trapping of psychotherapy within medical walls. For example Tom Rusk, the famous American psychiatrist, states in one of his bestselling books appropriately titled, *Instead of Therapy*:

> Although I am a psychiatrist, and therefore a medical doctor, I no longer believe that the language of science and medicine applies to the work that I do with my clients. I'm one of the growing number of psychological counselors who believe that psychological healing did not ever belong to the realm of medicine. The focus of all counseling is to help us learn to change our relationship with ourselves and others. I believe this kind of learning is really no different than any other deliberate learning ... Recognizing this process for what it is makes it clear that personal change – the only real "cure" for most psychological difficulties – is best considered an educational rather than a therapeutic enterprise.

Rusk goes on to strongly state that:

> "The mistaken identity" of therapy as a form of medical treatment is a fundamental error that has led to many misuses and abuses of professional caring relationships. (pp. xiv & xv)

Al-Balkhī: The Pioneer of Cognitive Therapy

The belief that it is our thinking that leads to our emotional state is as old as ancient Greek Stoic philosophy. However, it was al-Balkhī who developed this into a refined cognitive therapy. In considering faulty thinking that leads to emotional pathological habits of anxiety, anger and sadness, as the main reason behind the psychic disorders of the soul, al-Balkhī distinguishes himself as the pioneer or at least one of the earliest pioneers of this modern therapy. It has taken Western psychological sciences almost an entire century to arrive at this simple approach. After the failure of Freudian psychoanalysis as therapy became increasingly evident, western psychotherapy turned to behaviorism.

Abū Zayd al-Balkhī

The late fifties and early sixties of the twentieth century witnessed the rise of behavior therapy. Most therapists stopped discussing Freudian unconscious sexual and aggressive conflicts as the hidden causes behind neurotic disorders, and instead application of the works of Pavlov, Skinner and Wolpe became popular in therapy. Behavior therapy brought about a revolution in the treatment of simple phobias and disorders that could be shaped within its limited paradigm. According to this paradigm, psychological symptoms do not necessarily have any unconscious roots. They are simply learned habits that can directly be unlearnt and treated by conditioning. In other words, the neurosis is the symptom itself.

But then western therapists soon discovered that the simple, limited stimulus-response "Pepsi-cola vending machine" model of behaviorism was unable to deal with the more complex psychological problems of human beings. This was primarily due to neglect of the influence of thinking, beliefs and consciousness in the development of psychological disorders. Thus, an agonizing environmental experience is not necessarily a direct cause of emotional disorder, as behaviorists had believed, but rather it is how a person interprets the noxious experience that really lies at the cause of the problem. Meaning that the same painful experience encountered by two different people would bring about two different responses, according to the way in which they regard themselves and others.

The computer revolution has helped much in setting off what is now known as the cognitive revolution in psychology. Once a key is struck on a computer keyboard, it has to go through a central processing unit to give meaning to the action before appearing on the monitor. The same key may lead to a letter being written or if it is a game some object being moved. The software decides what effect the strike brings about. According to cognitive psychology, all our minds contain software that decides what an environmental experience really means. After the 1970s, cognitive therapists such as Beck, Ellis and Maulsby took the lead in western psychotherapy, and their cognitive approach is still the treatment of choice.

What is astonishing reading al-Balkhī's manuscript is the similarity between them, that is what these modern cognitive therapists say and do and what he theorized and applied. For example the well-known cognitive therapist, Aaron Beck states in his book, *Cognitive Therapy and the Emotional Disorders*:

> Psychological problems are not necessarily the product of mysterious, impenetrable forces (as Freud says) but may result from commonplace processes such as faulty learning, making incorrect inferences on the basis of inadequate or incorrect information, and not distinguishing adequately between imagination and reality. The behaviorist and the psychoanalyst have become aware that there are legitimate and important problems left unsolved by their neglect of the cognitive realm. (pp. 19-21).

He goes on to say:

> Private meanings are often unrealistic because the person does not have the opportunity to check their authenticity...The thesis that the special meaning of an event determines the emotional response forms the core of the cognitive model of emotions and emotional disorders. The meaning is encased in cognition, a thought or an image. (p.52)

Chapter two of the translated manuscript finds al-Balkhī recording that the body can lose its health from external factors such as severe heat or cold, or from internal factors, such as the imbalance of its humors. And in a similar way, he states, the health of the soul can also be affected by external or internal factors. External factors being what a person hears or sees in his environment i.e. fearful things or humiliating words, and internal factors being thinking that leads to anger, sadness or fear. In later chapters he discusses in detail how to eliminate emotional disorders by simply concentrating on changing one's inner thinking and irrational beliefs.

For example, in discussing fear and anxiety, al-Balkhī gives a number of vivid clinical examples illustrating anxiety related to future problems such as losing one's job or health, and fear or panic related to a phobia i.e. of thunder or death. After the exposition, he goes on to show that most things people are afraid of, are in fact not really harmful if thought through rationally and logically. He demonstrates this by reference to a great analogy: a fearful, panicky, neurotic Bedouin travels to a cold humid country and sees fog for the first time. He thinks the thick fog in front of him to be a solid impenetrable object. However, upon entering it he discovers its true nature: nothing more than humid air, no different to the air he was just breathing (p.307). Using cognitive rational therapy, he deduces that once treated neurotics would realize most of their fears and worries to be irrational, as harmless as fog!

In discussing cognitive therapy, al-Balkhī pursued a preventive approach and in doing so surpasses modern cognitive therapists who persistently talk about therapy. In a highly astute analogy he compares the body to the mind, suggesting that just as a healthy person keeps a stock of medicine always at hand for unexpected physical emergencies, he should also keep healthy thoughts and feelings in the mind for unexpected emotional outbursts. Such healthy thoughts and cognitions, he maintains, should be initiated and stored when a person is in a tranquil and relaxed condition. As the analogy makes clear, al-Balkhī's psychotherapy is mainly what could be termed today as "rational cognitive therapy".

Another highly fascinating feature of al-Balkhī's cognitive therapy which I did not find in modern literature is the use of one unacceptable cognition or emotion to change another, more incapacitating one. He gives the example of a soldier suffering from excessive anxiety and fear of combat. Such a soldier should remind himself of those heroic men who courageously led their troops to victory in fierce battles, and whose names have been recorded in history. By comparing his own shameful, emotional state with their great valor, he is bound to rouse anger at himself. This anger can then be further stimulated by the solider asserting to himself that panicky behavior of this sort is to be expected from the weak, cowardly men, women and children but not from brave adult fighters such as he. When the anger reaches a certain level it would neutralize his fear (p.308). So anger, which itself can be a disordered emotion, can be used against another more serious emotional pathology. In discussing this approach, al-Balkhī actually upgrades his form of cognitive therapy from limiting itself to changing the irrational content of thought to the process of thinking itself which reminds one of the contemporary third wave of cognitive therapy. This kind of therapy in which one uses a feeling or emotion to neutralize its opposite is termed by al-Balkhī and al-Ghazālī as *al-ʿilāj bi dhī* which literarily means treatment with the opposite. Indeed it clearly demonstrates the main fundamental nature of modern-day reciprocal inhibition which is one of the major techniques of behavior therapy.

Another important contribution, which is particularly relevant to Muslim psychotherapists, is Balkhī's Islamic oriented approach, which though not direct and sermonizing, is still influenced by the Islamic conceptions of human nature and the value of faith in Allah (SWT)* in cognitively alleviating symptoms of emotional disorder. He often reminds the depressed and anxiety ridden person that this world is neither the place of total happiness nor the place where one obtains all one's wishes and desires.

Al-Balkhī: The First to Discover the Difference Between Endogenous and Reactive Depression

Before concluding this foreword I ought to mention one of al-Balkhī's most surprising discoveries. Using astute observation and refined clinical sense, he was able to classify depression into three categories. The first being the everyday normal state of *ḥuzn* or sadness which afflicts all people everywhere (for this world, "is a place which cannot be lived without problems and deprivations"). It is a type of depression referred to in the most modern classification of psychiatric symptoms, DSM IV, as "normal depression". However, what makes al-Balkhī's discovery remarkable is his differentiation between his second and third categories of depression, for his perceptive clinical sense allowed him to clearly see the difference between endogenous and reactive depression.

This important discovery of differentiating between endogenous mental and psychological disorders, originating from within the body,

---

* (SWT) – *Subḥānahu wa Taʿālā*: May He be praised and may His transcendence be affirmed. Said when referring to God.

and those originating due to exogenous or environmental factors from outside the body, took a further ten centuries before inappropriately being credited to Emit Kraepelin whose work was only published towards the end of the nineteenth and the early years of the twentieth century. The modern disease model of contemporary psychiatry, recorded in the aforementioned latest classification known as the DSM IV, owes its origin to the nosological system originally developed by Kraepelin.

This classification has been very helpful to modern psychiatrists and clinical psychologists because in reality some forms of depression are caused by internal metabolic and biochemical abnormalities and do not seem to have clear environmental causes. Even when such precipitating life events are found, they do not justify the severity of the depressive responses which may include psychotic symptoms such as delusions and hallucinations. This is why endogenous depression was also referred to in the past as psychotic depression, today being known as major depression. Changing terminology in psychiatry may at times appear analogous to changes on a book cover, meaning that merchandise is kept the same with only external unnecessary changes made to its features. However, what concerns us here is that a patient suffering from major depression of this type may harbor symptoms of severe guilt, marked retardation, loss of pleasure, early morning wakefulness, a severely subjective depressive mood, anorexia and weight loss, and false beliefs and perceptions. This kind of endogenous depression often requires hospitalization and treatment with potent drugs and in very severe cases, electro convulsive therapy.

Reactive depression, on the other hand, is clearly caused by an environmental factor involving morbid thoughts and feelings about a real or anticipated loss or stressful life event. The reactive, or what was once known as the neurotically depressed person, does not suffer from any psychotic symptoms such as delusions or hallucinations nor does he/she lose touch with reality, and generally does not need to be hospitalized. His depressive symptoms are milder and can respond to cognitive therapy treatment. If antidepressant drugs are prescribed, they are best taken to enhance cognitive therapy.

This conception of depression as endogenous and reactive is not only supported by clinical observation and recent biochemical and hereditary research, but also by experimental studies in which patients of both types were asked to respond to tests and questionnaires. Plotted on a graph the results took the form of a bimodal curve confirming the existence of two different groups in the same tested sample. And though the latest DSM IV classifications do not include the terms "endogenous" and "reactive", since its authors did their best to picture depression as a continuum, non-American psychiatrists and clinical psychologists in many parts of the world refuse to abandon this classification because they are more useful in showing the difference between them and other forms of depressive reactions such as manic-depressive or bipolar depression and involutional melancholia.

Although the chapter on sadness and depression has been translated and included in this work, I wish to present readers here with a simplified version to emphasize Balkhī's remarkable clinical insight and tremendous findings with regards to the differentiation between endogenous and reactive depressions. To follow are translated extracts taken from pages 316 to 319:

> *Ḥuzn*, sadness or depression, is of two kinds. The (environmental) causes, for one of them is clearly known, such as the loss of a loved relative, bankruptcy or loss of something the depressed person values greatly. The other type has no known reasons. It is a sudden affliction of sorrow and distress *ghummah*, which persists all the time preventing the afflicted person from physical activity or from showing any happiness or enjoying any of the pleasures or *shahwah* (food and sex). The patient does not know any clear reasons for his lack of activity and distress. This type of *ḥuzn* or depression with no known reasons is caused by bodily symptoms such as impurity of the blood and other changes in it. Its treatment is a physical medical one which aims at purifying the blood....

Thus, for this type of endogenous depression, al-Balkhī clearly points to physical medical management as the main form of treatment. He does not recommend cognitive psychotherapy because the patient may not benefit from it since the underlying etiology is organic. However he does not forget to recommend other forms of psychological therapy which can bring about pleasure and happiness to the endoge-nously depressed person. He states:

> Help should be limited to bringing about happiness and pleasure through friendly companionship, pleasant conversation and other activities which may stimulate the person to reduce his agony such as listening to music and songs. (p.317)

On the other hand, for reactive depression, an "external" and "internal" concentrated program of cognitive therapy is clearly recom-mended. *Ḥuzn* sadness with known reasons is caused by thoughts directed on loss of a loved thing or the difficulty of attaining a greatly desired thing. And it is this particular type of sadness and its treatment that we wish to discuss in this chapter. The therapy for *ḥuzn* is external and internal. The external consisting of persuasive talk, preaching and advising. The treatment resembles medication given to the physically sick. The internal therapy consists of development of the inner thought and cognition of the depressed patient to help him eliminate his depres-sive thought patterns. Through therapy the patient must realize the physical psychosomatic harm which the depressive mood is causing to his health, and since his own self should be the thing most dear to him, it will indeed be greatly irrational to harm the most beloved for losing things that can be substituted. Al-Balkhī states that this would be akin to a merchant "who on losing a little profit stupidly pays his capital to regain it...."

Al-Balkhī goes on to recommend a number of other cognitive strategies a therapist could use to counteract the negative thoughts causing this type of neurotic depression, i.e. internally realizing that those who succumb to depression and refuse to fight it are weak and failures in life, whereas those who patiently resist negative thoughts and to face problems with renewed optimism are strong and success-ful. The depressed person should ask himself which of the two groups he would want to identify with and belong to, "the 'failed' or the 'suc-cessful'?" According to al-Balkhī, losing one's perseverance is a greater catastrophe than losing what one is depressed about.

Although more than eleven centuries old, the manuscript is written in an easy, simple and lucid Arabic style, beautifully elucidating spiritually and psychologically cognitive ways of treating anxiety, panic, anger, depression and obsessive disorder. Any Arabic speaking reader would be able to understand its content without the help of a dictionary or a tutor. In translating the work I have done my best to preserve the simplicity of the original Arabic language but whenever necessary have added a few words to make the text clearer, these additions have been placed in parenthesis. Furthermore I have added 40 footnotes where relevant to compare al-Balkhī's work with modern psychotherapy.

I hope that the publication of the translation of this valuable manuscript will help modern scholars to rewrite the history of psychology and psychotherapy. Sadly, all too often Western historians of psychology generally start with the Greeks, then leap forward to the Renaissance and the age of European Enlightenment, bypassing the Middle Ages and the contributions of the Islamic world as if no other civilizations had existed. The silence is astonishing! For example, Marx and Hillix's famous reference on the systems and theories of psychology (Marx & Hillix, 1979), contains a comprehensive and detailed chapter on the emergence of modern psychology, in which prominent Greek figures such as Pythagoras, Socrates, Plato, Aristotle and Euclid (who lived from the sixth century B.C, to the third century C.E.) are honored, with a subsequent 15 century jump to Roger Bacon (1214–1294). The same approach, and silence, prevails in other books on the history of psychology, i.e. Leahy (1992) and Hergenhahn (2009). Even when mentioned, the contributions of the Muslim scholars and physicians are very briefly cited. I hope this work serves to rectify this, at least in the field of psychology, and give credit where credit is due.

Malik Badri, *The Translator*

PROFESSOR OF PSYCHOLOGY
Ahfad University, Omdurman, Sudan

Abū Zayd al-Balkhī

REFERENCES

Abū Zayd al-Balkhī, *Maṣāliḥ al-Abdān wa al-Anfus*, [Sustenance for Bodies and Souls]. Reproduced from Manuscript No. 3741, Ayasofya Library, Istanbul, by Fuat Sezgin (Frankfurt: Institute for the History of Arabic-Islamic Science, 1984).

Badri, M.B., "Abu Zayd Albalkhi: A genius whose psychiatric contributions needed more than ten centuries to be appreciated," *Malaysian Journal of Psychiatry*, vol. 6, no. 2, September issue, 1998.

Badri, M.B. & Ashwi M., Al-Balkhī's *Maṣāliḥ al-Abdān wa al-Anfus*, (In Arabic). (Riyadh: King Faisal Islamic Research Centre, 2002).

Beck, Aaron, *Cognitive Therapy and the Emotional Disorders*. (New York: New American Library 1976).

Benson, Herbert, *Timeless Healing: The Power and Biology of Belief*. (London: Simon & Schuster, 1960).

Leahey, T., *A History of Psychology: Main Currents in Psychological Thought*. (New Jersey: Pearson Prentice Hall, 1992).

Marx, M. & Hillix, W., *Systems and Theories in Psychology*. (New York: McGraw-Hill, 1979).

Rusk, Tom. *Instead of Therapy: Help Yourself Change and Change the Help You're Getting* (California: Hay House, Inc., 1991).

The Complete Translation of
Al-Balkhī's *Sustenance of the Soul*

Translation and Annotation by
Malik Badri (Ph.D., F.B.Ps.S., C.Psychol.)
Professor of Psychology, Ahfad University, Sudan

Al-Balkhī's Introduction to His Manuscript

*In the Name of Allah
the Most Beneficent and the Most Merciful*

My second essay (or part) of this book: *Sustenance of the Soul* falls into eight chapters: the first chapter is on elucidating the need for promoting the sustenance of the soul. The second chapter is on endeavoring to keep perpetuating the health of the soul. The third chapter is on making an effort to bring back the healthy condition of the soul if it loses it. The fourth chapter is on specifying and classifying the psychological symptoms (disorders) and enumerating them. The fifth is on suppressing anger and rage and obliterating them. The sixth chapter is on the methods used to tranquilize fear and panic. The seventh is on the methods of managing sadness and depression, and the eighth chapter is on how to ward off obsessions of the chest (heart) and the (harmful or negative) inner speech of the soul.

CHAPTER [1] *Exposing the Great Need for Promoting the Sustenance of Souls*

IN THE FIRST PART of this book we elucidated the knowledge and the practices required for the sustenance (health) of the body by preserving its wellbeing when healthy and reviving it back to health if affected by symptoms of (physical) disorder and disease. We also gave a comprehensive presentation, that informs the reader on how his body can benefit from the consumption of healthy food and medicines to perpetuate safety and guarantee health. In this second part of the book, we endeavor to give an explanation concerning the sustenance of the soul and how to keep its components in a state of wellbeing and harmony in order to avoid the psychological symptoms that it may face.

We start by saying that since man is composed of a body and soul, he is bound to face from each part of them fitness or weakness, health or sickness or other symptoms that afflict his health in a negative way. The symptoms that afflict the body and upset its wellbeing are those such as fever, headaches, and various kinds of pains that affect the organs. The psychological symptoms that afflict a person are those such as anger, sorrow, fear, panic and other similar manifestations.

These psychological symptoms affect man much more frequently than bodily symptoms. Indeed some people may almost never suffer from any or most bodily symptoms throughout or most of their lives. In contrast, psychological symptoms induce man to suffer from them most of the time. Indeed no man is saved in all his conditions from feelings of distress, anger, sadness or similar psychological symptoms. However people differ with respect to the intensity of their feelings in response to these symptoms. This is so because each person responds according to his temperament and the foundation of his constitution with respect to strength or weakness. Some may be quick to become angry (hot-tempered) and some slow. Similarly some may respond with excessive fear and panic when accosted with fearful things and some with endurance and courage. And so one can differentiate between the expected responses of women and children and those with weak dispositions in comparison to those with a strong natural disposition; each person will respond according to the degree of his predisposition whether it is high or low or whether he finds the situation difficult to stand or weak in its effect.

For this reason no man should be heedless of being concerned with the sustenance of his soul or neglectful in making an effort to shield it from disturbance and anxiety which leads to an unhappy life. Such psychological symptoms can thus be comparable to bodily symptoms that cause a person pain and illness and result in an agonizing situation.

This discussion (on the sustenance of the soul) is not generally mentioned by physicians nor documented in their written books on medicine, the sustenance of the body and treatment of its physical ailments. This is because it is a subject not within their professional interest and because the treatment of psychological symptoms does not match the remedies they give (to patients) such as bloodletting, medicine and other similar treatments. However, even if they do not take psychological treatment into consideration and their habitual ways have lead to their ignoring it, the approach of adding means for sustenance of souls to the sustenance of bodies is an appropriate, correct one. Indeed it is a much needed (therapeutic) approach which can be beneficial due to the interaction between the workings of the soul with those of the body. Man's stamina is a combination of both his body and soul and one cannot imagine that he can exist without this dual combination which causes him to act as a human being. Their combination gives to man his ability to respond to threatening issues and painful symptoms.

Thus, when the body becomes ill, is in pain and subjected to harmful things, it will even prevent those with strong disposition from proper understanding and learning and other (mental activities), or performing duties in a proper manner. And when the soul is afflicted (with psychological pain) the body will lose its natural ability to enjoy pleasure and will find its life becoming distressed and disturbed. Not only that, but psychological pain may lead to bodily illnesses. And if this is so, then every person has a real need, particularly those who frequently suffer from harmful psychological symptoms, to know how to deal with them in order to treat them or reduce their harmful effect. And if such a person finds this information in a book alongside other information about how to treat his physical ailments then he would benefit greatly as he need not be left to search for treatments in the different books of physicians and scholars of wisdom and religious sermons. It is a great assistance to him to have all this information compiled in one book that he can refer to.

Moreover, it is known that obtaining knowledge with respect to management of a body's sustenance through maintaining its wellbeing and returning it to health, if this is lost, is not an easy matter. Although many books have been written by physicians detailing this bodily sustenance, it seems that their aim is not to make this knowledge available to the lay reader. On the contrary, in writing the section of our book on the sustenance of the body, we have followed an easy abbreviated style that takes the form of simple reminders of guidance and advice. As for our section on the sustenance of the soul, we do not know of anybody (before us) that has written on the subject and explained its contents according to the needs (of the reader). On this matter, we speak according to our knowledge and Allah is the one who grants success.

CHAPTER [2] *Sustenance of Psychological Health*

THE HUMAN SOUL can be healthy or unhealthy in the same way that its body can be healthy or unhealthy. When the soul is healthy, all its faculties will be tranquil without any psychological symptoms manifesting such as anger, panic, depression and others that we have enumerated. This tranquility of the soul is its healthy condition and that of its safety, just as the health of the body and its safety lies in the tranquility and balance of its humors, so that the blood, the yellow and black bile and the phlegm are all calm and serene and none of them overpowers the other. And just as we stated (in the first part) concerning the sustenance of the body that one must first start by making an effort to preserve and sustain one's health, if healthy, and then follow this with returning oneself back to health, if one loses it, similarly, for promoting the wellbeing of the soul one must start by maintaining its health, if healthy, by securing the serenity of its faculties, or regaining its health if lost. So one who wishes to preserve the calmness and harmony of his soul should avoid stirring up any of its faculties.

As previously mentioned, the body can preserve its health in two ways (external and internal), i.e. protection from external hazards such as (extreme) heat or cold or other calamities, and protection from internal imbalances, so that none of the four humors overrun the other. This balance can be achieved by modifying one's diet; taking what is beneficial and avoiding what is harmful as well as employing the other advice mentioned in the first part of the book. Likewise, the health of the soul can also be maintained in these two (external and internal) ways. Externally is to protect the soul from outside elements such as what a person hears or sees that may worry or disturb him causing arousal of emotions that include anger, panic, sadness or fear and other similar responses.

Internally means to protect the soul from internal symptoms of negative thinking[3] about what may harm the person with respect to the symptoms or disorders that we have described. As is known, these disorders can cause worry and anxiety to enter the heart. One can heal oneself using two methods. First, when feeling peaceful and when the faculties of the soul are in a tranquil state, one should convince the heart (mind) that this world, *dunyā*, has not been created to give people whatever they wish or desire without their being subjected to anxieties and worries or harmful unwelcome symptoms. One should realize (after this internal monologue of self-convincing) that this is the inherent nature of life on this earth and that this is what one should expect from life in developing one's habits and a regular way of life. Therefore one should not ask for what has not been created in the very nature of one's world.[4]

---

3 Notice his cognitive approach of considering negative harmful thoughts and beliefs as the cause of psychological disorders.

4 The modern psychotherapist should notice that in this statement, al-Balkhī has used four therapeutic techniques. First by asking the emotionally disordered to choose the time in which he is fully relaxed and tranquil to remind himself that his worldly troubles are only natural and expected. Second, his use of the very modern technique known as reciprocal inhibition not only shows his great skill as a cognitive therapist, but also as

This should be the basic tenet in one's social relations with those who are above, equal to or below one in status, and furthermore one should, as much as one can tolerate, learn to ignore the annoying (anxiety-provoking) elements that one experiences. A person should train himself not to overreact to the minor incidents or things that he hears or sees. When he trains himself to tolerate these little irritating experiences, this will (in time) become habitual and he will then be able to tolerate things that are more frustrating and experiences that are more annoying. In doing so he will be analogous to one who (gradually) trains himself to tolerate the painful effects of a slight increase in temperature, heat or cold, as well as other minor bodily pains, without showing impatience or tension until this becomes part of his usual habits. This will then help him to endure the test of greater pain if he were to encounter it. This approach is the way to train the body and is the same approach to train the soul.5

Having said this, it must be noted that any person using this approach to face the problems and difficult experiences which may befall him should be aware of the degree of forbearance which his soul can bear. Every individual has a different level of endurance; the strength of his heart or its weakness (in facing anxiety) and the breadth of his chest or its constricted nature (in facing frustration with patience.)6 Some can withstand great calamities without being stirred up, and are able to continuously deal with each problem and treat it or reduce its harmful effects by trying different methods. Some however are traumatized or succumb to the slightest emotional provocation

a behavior therapist. In reciprocal inhibition the noxious stimuli are repeatedly associated with psychologically relaxing responses until a bond is created between them and consequently, the painful stimuli lose their ability to stimulate anxiety. The same method, in a graded fashion is used in systematic desensitization therapy. Third, he uses rational cognitive therapy to change the thinking and beliefs of the disordered person. Fourth he uses a psycho-spiritual religious cognitive approach in reminding the patient that this world is naturally a place of expected anxiety and sadness. It is in the Hereafter that people will really be happy. This is in fact an application of the acceptance and mindfulness approach of the third wave of cognitive therapy.

5 Again, al-Balkhī speaks like a behavior therapist using the gradual hierarchy of systematic desensitization therapy. Notice his brilliant comparisons between the psyche and the soma.

6 Notice his insight in individual differences in emotionality.

consequently losing their ability to reduce tension or solve the problem they are faced with by recourse to available methods. This could even lead them to develop a bodily disorder.7 If a person comes to know the nature of his soul and the degree to which it can tolerate stress in dealing with problems, then he can decide, based on this knowledge, what kinds of problems he is ready to face and what problems he should avoid. This principle is applicable to all, whether a king or a commoner.

If one finds that one is strong enough to face great problems which would normally cause others much trouble and anxiety, then one can proceed to bravely confront them. If on the other hand one realizes that they may be too much for one's weak disposition, then one should keep away from them even if this results in deprivation of certain pleasures and anticipated wishes. To be deprived of expected pleasures if this means maintenance of the soul's tranquility, is far better than confronting what one cannot tolerate. Choosing to confront ordeals of this type would certainly cause much anxiety and distress which may result in an emotional or even physical disorder of the body. However, wisely steering clear of what one cannot endure, will lead to a peaceful life, a healthy soul and real worldly happiness.

CHAPTER [3] *Ways of Regaining Psychological Health When One Loses It*

WHAT WE HAVE MENTIONED in the last chapter concerning the health and tranquility of the soul, is a state that cannot be attained

---

7 Al-Balkhī, more than 11 centuries ago, arrived at the fact that intense emotional reactions such as anxiety and depression can lead to physical illness. We now know that such emotional disorders do not only lead to the classic psychosomatic disorders like ulcers and migraine, but to all sorts of physical disorders. When one is caught up for a long time in stressful conditions, his or her adrenal glands will pour out andrenocortical hormones that cause the autonomic nervous system to be in a state of emergency. As time passes, the person will develop high blood pressure and his immunity against diseases will be greatly weakened. This renders the patient vulnerable to all kinds of diseases and physical disorders such as elevated blood pressure, gastrointestinal disorders and cancer.

at all times. By his very nature, it is not possible for man to keep his soul in perpetual tranquility and peace without being subjected to anger, fear, distress and similar psychological symptoms.[8] This world (*dunyā*) is the abode of anxiety, sadness, worry and calamity. So it is only normal for man to expect, in spite of his efforts, the onslaught of misfortune or even calamity to disturb the calmness of his soul. In a similar vein man cannot escape the bodily affliction of all manner of aches and pains and even were he to be spared the more serious illnesses and diseases, it is not conceivable that he would be saved from minor bodily symptoms.

And if this much can be said of bodily symptoms, then we must affirm that the affliction of psychological symptoms is much more common. One may live for a very long time without complaining of bodily aches or pains, but it is unlikely that one will pass a day without experiencing something that causes anger, anxiety, sadness or gloom. This is due to the intrinsic essential nature of the soul and its volatile essence and changeability.[9] And it is for this reason that man should do his utmost best to protect the soul from (external and internal) emotionally disturbing events and keep it in its best possible condition. And just as when the body is afflicted with painful symptoms or illnesses, it can only be helped by treatments similar to it in its physical nature such as medicines or special diets that bring about its cure; so the treatment of the disordered soul that complains of psychological symptoms requires a spiritual (psychic) kind of therapy that is similar to its nonphysical nature.

Furthermore, just as the body can be treated either internally through i.e. prevention of certain foods or externally through i.e. the use of medicines and special diets, so the soul can also be treated through these internal and external approaches. One suffering from psychological disturbance can fight his symptoms internally by

[8] Notice that al-Balkhī uses the term "symptom" (in Arabic, ʿaradh, plural aʿrādh)' for what we consider in modern-day classification as "disorder".

[9] Al-Balkhī here refers to the Islamic conception about the ethereal nature of the soul as spiritual. The commanding center of the soul or *nafs* is the heart (*qalb*) that is described by the Prophet as more changeable than boiling water in a pot. (The hadith was authenticated by Aḥmad ibn Ḥanbal).

developing within the soul thoughts (of an opposite nature to the ones that sustain the problem) that neutralize the symptoms and desensitize their provocation. Externally, one can listen to the advice of another whose (therapeutic) discussion (or counseling) would calm the agitated soul and treat its abnormality.

So a person who cares about the health of his soul should spare no effort in benefiting from these two (internal and external) means to protect the soul from being dominated by negative psychological symptoms that upset his life. It is vital to do so, since the psychological symptoms may become severe and lead to bodily disorders.

Additionally, we see that just as in treating bodily illnesses the external help one receives from therapeutic diets or a physician's prescription is more useful than a person's own internal treatment such as preventing consumption of certain foods, so it is with respect to psychological disorders. That is, the benefit one obtains externally from advice and counseling is more useful than a person's internal attempt (at treatment) through generating his own therapeutic thoughts. This is due to two reasons. First, man in general accepts from others what he does not accept from himself. His reasoning and thought are intermixed with his passions, each implicated by the other. Second, one suffering painful psychological symptoms is so occupied and overpowered by them that he cannot clearly think how to overcome them. He needs others to show him the way to recovery. In that he is like a physician who falls ill to the extent that he fails to diagnose and treat himself, needing another doctor to treat him. It is for this reason that many judicious kings (and sensible rulers) appoint special wise advisors to help them with their psychological symptoms, to council them, calm their anger and rage, and tranquilize their fears and anxieties. They accept their advice and make use of it. They also employ astute experienced physicians to treat them for physical illness and complaints. They appreciate the need for both medical and psychological healing by mainly being helped by their external benefits.

However, with regards to the earlier statement, that the external aspects of treatment such as medicines prescribed by physicians and advice provided by wise counselors are superior to internal aspects, it must be emphasized that both treatments are not mutually exclusive. One should not forget or underestimate the value of the internal means in treatment. As already mentioned, the internal method employed to deal with psychological symptoms concerns a person generating (positive) thoughts within his soul to aid him in suppressing the symptoms and desensitizing their agitation. These tranquil thoughts and beliefs should not only be generated during the illness. They can be nurtured and developed during times of psychological health and relaxation and stored in memory in order to bring them back to consciousness whenever one is afflicted with emotional symptoms. These (internal) thoughts will be one's first source of aid if there exists no (external) wise person to help with the symptoms. This is equivalent to the storage of medicine with established worth in a first aid kit to use in case of unexpected bodily pain developing in the absence of a physician. So, we shall delineate in this part of our book all the advice and methods that can be used to treat the psychological disorders that we shall detail in the following chapter, so that with the Grace of Allah, everyone can benefit from them whenever there is a need.

CHAPTER [4] *Enumerating the Psychological Symptoms (Disorders) and Specifying their Distinguishing Attributes*

SINCE WE HAVE DISCUSSED the methods of dealing with the psychological symptoms in a general manner (in earlier chapters), it is binding on us (in this chapter) to describe the nature of these symptoms in detail in the manner that physicians do. In preparing their medical texts, they first describe and specify the different bodily symptoms and then explain how to treat each one of them. We begin by saying that the features attributed to the human soul are quite diverse. Some of them are virtuous such as the intellect, the faculty of comprehension and the faculty of retention and memory, whilst others in contrast are blameworthy attributes. Also, attributed to the soul are some praiseworthy characteristics such as chastity, munificence and generosity as well as in contrast some blameworthy characteristics opposed to them.

However, the soul may also be subjected to transitory conditions that are different from the permanent traits that we have described. These are the emotional states such as anger, fear and similar symptoms. Our interest in this book is to deal with these symptoms that appear and disappear in a way that agitate the soul and cause the body to be stirred up (perturbed), at times in a harmful manner. As is known, each symptom has a specific effect on the body, causing it to be greatly altered. For example, the influence of excessive anger and rage is clearly apparent in incoherent speech, trembling and facial changes, including the color of the skin. In a similar way, fear and anxiety can change the temperature of the body instigating it to be hotter or cooler and distorting its facial expressions. So the person who cares about the health of his body should do his best to calm the agitated state of these symptoms in a way that saves him from their harmful effects.

We believe that at the core of all harmful emotional symptoms lies distress or anxiety, *al-gham*. It is like the root with the rest, its branches. It is the starting point of all symptoms and their augmenter. For example, before he experiences rage and anger, a person first feels anxiety and distress concerning the situation that triggers the anger. Similarly, it is distress or anxiety over a fearful situation that precedes the symptom of fear and terror.[10]

The opposite state of this distress is happiness and joyfulness which is also the root cause of all the positive emotional states that a person experiences such as tranquility, pleasure and delight. Thus anxiety, distress and happiness are the opposite poles of the root causes of all pleasing and tormenting symptoms. Therefore distress and anxiety are the most powerful causes of the psychological illness of the soul and joy and happiness are the main basis of its health. Thus, if one is keen concerning the sustenance of one's soul, then one should do one's best to shield it from distress and to lead it to joyfulness in the same manner that one who is keen with regards to his physical health will avoid

[10] This is one of the verifications for the astute clinical observations of al-Balkhī. Modern psychologists view stress with its three major categories of frustration, conflict and pressure as the major root cause for anxiety and mood disorders.

those things that would lead to disease and take those that would enhance one's health.

Having said this, we assert that anger is one of the negative symptoms of the soul that is generated from distress. Rage and anger can agitate the soul and the body in a way that no other symptom can do. When a person is in a state of rage and fury, he embeds himself in a condition of nervousness that increases circulation of the blood, changes his color, raises body temperature and causes him to perform uncontrollable movements. In extreme cases he may look like a madman.

A second negative symptom of the soul is terror. It afflicts a person when he is exposed to a fearful thing or situation. Excessive fear can lead to terror and panic. In this severe anxiety state, the color of the person will become yellowish because the blood rushes from the surface of the body to the internal organs and the hands and legs will shake uncontrollably, failing to perform their natural function. Furthermore, the person may lose the ability to think properly to the extent of failing to find a solution to rescue him from the frightening object or situation. This critical condition would disturb the bodies humors, causing them to function abnormally and may eventually cause a severe bodily ailment. This terror develops from the fear that overwhelms a person if he thinks or imagines a scary thing (or more so) if he actually sees or experiences it. This fear and anxiety can also be caused by a person hearing an earsplitting sound that he cannot tolerate or from hearing news that contains a terrifying message.

A third symptom is excessive sadness, depression or melancholy. It is a symptom which afflicts a person due to the loss of something he likes or loves, the deprivation (of which) results in sadness or grief. If the sadness or grief increases in intensity, it then becomes outright depression and melancholy. A person suffering from this extreme state will succumb to hopelessness and impatience, described by the Arabic word *jazaᶜ*.[11] So fear and anxiety to panic and terror is like sadness is

[11] There is no precise translation in English to the Arabic word "*jazaᶜ*" because it implies excessive sadness, grief or depression plus the inability of the person to endure his calamity. It is the impatience of the person that is associated more with the term *jazaᶜ* than the actual severity of the loss he incurs.

to critical grief and depression since terror and panic are the extreme form of fear and depression and *jaza'* is the extreme form of sadness. The states of hopelessness and impatience, a consequence of such intense levels of sadness and grief, are often associated with certain very unpleasant reactions. The person suffering may slap his face, tear at his clothes and pull his hair behaving like someone who has lost his mind or his integrity. Similar to the symptoms of terror, this condition may also lead to serious bodily symptoms, whose dangers the depressed person in the total grip of this emotional state may not be aware of.

The fourth psychological symptom or disorder is obsession. Its persistence in the human heart (or mind) causes repetitive repulsive or immoral thoughts that result in apprehension and unhappiness to the extent that the one obsessed may lose his ability to enjoy the pleasures of the body and the soul. This symptom of obsession is what is referred to (in Islamic jurisprudence) as the inner speech or whispers of the soul.

These are the four symptoms of the soul that have a connection with the workings of the body and which when aggravated can cause physical illness and bodily harm. Akin to the pain and aches of the body's organs which deprive the soul from enjoying food and psychological pleasures. Accordingly, just as the sustenance of the body necessitates treatment using medicines and special potions to heal the pain, the healing of the soul requires the application of the methods we described previously in a general way. We will elucidate, with the permission of Allah, in the following chapters how to treat each of these (four) psychological symptoms in a way that heals them and counteract their harmful effects.

CHAPTER [5] *How to Counteract Anger and Get Rid of It*

IT IS PERTINENT to start (our detailed discussion on treating psychological disorders) with the symptom of anger since it is the most frequent in upsetting all people, disturbing its victims almost every day of their lives. Whether an individual is a commoner with limited authority over members of the family and servants, or a king or sultan ruling over subjects, he will regardless be strongly affected by anger whenever faced with disrespect or insubordination. Anger is more common and extreme if a person is by nature intolerant and hot tempered. In such cases, it can be a chronic symptom that controls one's behavior. A person of this type greatly needs to protect the soul against its ill effects so that his life is not subjected to stress and unhappiness. By healing the soul of this chronic symptom the sufferer will save himself from the guilt and repentance entailed by his uncontrollable rage and outbursts. This applies to everybody, whether a king with the authority to inflict severe punishment or a normal person with limited power. Indeed, the greater one's authority over others the greater the danger of one's outbursts.

Thus those most in need of training themselves to counteract anger are kings and rulers, and to heal their anger such persons will require both an external adviser and an internal self-treatment approach. With regards to the external line of attack, the influential person should select and appoint wise men from his favorite companions to be with him (most of the time) and to permit them to counsel him, remind him (about the harmful aspects of uncontrolled anger) and enlighten him concerning the righteousness of forgiveness and its good outcome among his people in this world as well as its boundless reward in the hereafter. He should also allow these men to politely intercede in the case of dealing with wrongdoers who may be brutally punished during a fit of uncontrollable emotional outburst. This merciful intercession may cool rage, like pouring cold water over boiling water. For this reason sensible kings have always kept wise men around them in special or public meetings. The internal approach is based on mental maneuvering of thoughts, consciously repeated to counteract anger-laden thinking. One of the mental maneuvers involves taking advantage of moments of relaxation and tranquility to convince oneself that anger is a symptom that can be resisted (with calm, serene thinking) on its first appearance. Because if not opposed (nipped in the bud) when it first begins, it will blow up into full-scale irrepressible rage, and cannot be contained after this.[12] This is

12 In this, al-Balkhī's refined clinical sense has led him to the most recent results of researches that counteract the once accepted theory of catharsis in relieving anger. It

analogous to a fire which starting off small can easily be put out with a little effort, but which if allowed to continue unrestrained, will burst into flames destroying whatever is flammable around it. Or take the example of a horse that begins to run amok with its rider, if the rider does not firmly bolt it as soon as it starts to run riot, he will not be able to control it. Keeping this thought in mind, when a person first feels anger creeping into his soul, he can prevent it from leading him into uncontainable rage. With repeated exercise this will become a useful future habit.

A second mental tactic is to contemplate bodily disorders that can be caused by anger and rage. Rising temperature, trembling, apprehension, arousal and other general bodily disturbances are among the obvious symptoms. One should think sensibly about the physical bodily dangers that can accrue from this heightened state. A person may end up with an incurable bodily disorder. In this case, suffering more harm than the hurt he would wish to inflict on the one making him angry in the first place. So instead of getting even with the latter what he actually does is to injure more himself. If one thinks deeply along this line, then when anger does begin to creep into the soul, one will be more able to control oneself and heal the rising emotion.

An additional mental exercise is to reflect on the intense feelings of guilt and remorse that many kings and authoritative people have suffered from when they have allowed their anger to boil to the point of inflicting extremely harsh punishments on the source of their rage. They may be unable to remedy the situation (for example in the case of a sentence involving capital punishment) resulting in the whole episode causing them much possible suffering in this world and in the hereafter. One should thus guard oneself from repeating such reckless emotional actions. Deep reflection on this would train one to be more skillful in controlling one's anger and in being careful and unhurried

---

was widely accepted that expressing anger would blow off steam and lessen its effect. Psychologists believe now that the application of this pressure cooker hypothesis may actually increase anger rather than decreasing it. After summarizing modern research, Carlson & Hatfield state that, "...when people express their anger, aggressive feelings, they often get themselves so worked up that the situation may become worse than it was before" (1992).

in deciding what kind of measures to take against those who are the source of the anger. Furthermore, one will avoid any actions that will give one possible cause to repent in the future.

Another aspect of positive thinking is to remind the thinking soul of the great virtues of patience and forgiveness. Forgiveness is one of the noblest human virtues of kings and rulers. Those whose character displays this virtue, that is of having control over anger, being able to suppress rage and pardon offenders, are the ones who will be widely remembered and whose tales will be recorded for all to read and emulate. One who wishes to heal his anger should ask himself whether it is better to emulate such gracious models of forgiveness or to execute vengeance exposing the soul to the expected pain of regret and remorse. If one brings such thoughts into one's consciousness upon the onset of anger seeping into the soul, one will benefit much from them.

One more mental maneuver is to realize that quick, severe vengeance and reprimand would surely end up detrimental to the intimate warm relation between a superior and his subordinates and servants, and between a king and his subjects. It is true that such harsh measures would make the subordinates and subjects obedient, but this kind of submission would only be external in nature. Internally this harsh action and unnecessary rebuking would breed animosity and bitterness.

On the other hand, gentleness, overlooking minor mistakes and forgiveness would fill the hearts of the servants and subjects with genuine love and mercy. Their obedience to the superior or king would be internal in nature. It is the submission born of love that causes them to be their protectors and defenders whether they know of it or not. But external obedience is that of fear and resentment. In such a case, the boss or king, instead of expecting support from his juniors or subjects, would be cautious and on his guard from them.

Indeed, there is a very great difference between these two forms of compliance, and the one who endeavors to heal his anger should take heed from this.

Actually, if a person is angered by one of his subordinates whom he can punish or rebuke whenever he wishes, it would seem unwise to allow himself to react with unmanageable rage that could be harmful to him. A sensible and judicious approach is to delay his emotional response until the fury calms and then to fairly weigh the offense and decide on the suitable punishment. Such a line of attack would give him benefit in two merits. First he would attain the attributes of patience and forgiveness, and second he would be more successful in changing the behavior of his subordinate by choosing a suitable punishment for the kind of offense committed. In commenting about this gracious approach, a noble King is quoted to have said, "Why should I be angry concerning what I own and why should I be angry at what I do not own".[13] If one remembers this idea it will help to neutralize one's angry feelings.

Yet another way to counteract anger and rage is to concentrate one's negative feelings towards the wrong deed of the subordinate or subject concerned, and not towards the offender as a human being. This would allow the angry person to thus resist any unjust oppressive behavior, and also lead him to discover that most of these offenses are either the result of irresistible lust, or the inability to do what is expected as a result of some tempting desire. He should then come to realize that nobody, whether subordinate or head, subject or king, is spared such incitements and motives. This should also in turn naturally lead him to sympathize with the offender due to (understanding) the latter's weakness with respect to his lust and desire. If he gives himself time to contemplate the matter, he may even begin to have mercy on the one upon whom his revenge was about to be levelled.

Furthermore, he can genuinely ask himself whether or not in his own past he had committed the same kind of mistakes and careless behavior making him angry at the present. He would surely find that in fact he had committed either similar or greater errors due to seductive lust and desires. He would also feel bitter about those who

---

[13] Al-Balkhī did not explain this ambiguous statement by this noble king. From what he has discussed it seems that the king meant that everything belongs to Allah and that all of what he owns and do not own belong to Allah and accordingly a wise Muslim should not be so angry because of things that he does not own in the first place.

punished him at the time. Thus it would seem unjustifiable to punish somebody for a fault that one has undertaken oneself. This type of thinking and these types of tactics will surely help one to calm down.

Additionally, if an angry person thoughtfully reminds himself of the wrongdoer's past sincere services and good characteristics, he is bound to reduce negative feelings towards him. However he should avoid seeing the person concerned while still emotionally provoked, as doing so before feelings cool down may rouse the anger that had started to dissipate. It is better to avoid any encounter for a few days since the passage of time can heal any stirred emotion. If it is anger, it will reduce and if it is sadness its effects will diminish. This is particularly effective if the time in question is used to listen to guidance from a wise counselor combined with inner constructive thinking and healing maneuvers. This, with the Grace of Allah, would save the angry person from the harmful feelings and possible actions that he could have experienced or practiced without the help of our healing tactics.

CHAPTER [6] *Tranquilizing Fear*

WE HAVE ALREADY MENTIONED the adverse effects of fear and its harmful consequences on the body and how such disturbance if not checked, can have extremely serious physical consequences. We have also mentioned that terror is an extreme form of fear since not everything or situation that causes fear would reach the level of terror or panic. What terrorizes a person and agitates his soul is something that is quite threatening to him, that he thinks about or hears or sees. To cause terror or panic, the alarming object or frightening situation must be either directly perceived or expected to turn up or occur in a short time. A fearful object or occurrence that is not directly observed or that is expected to take place after a long time would not cause fear but rather distress and worry. For example a young man who thinks about the unquestionable impending issue of becoming old and dying may feel dejected and sad, but not afraid and unduly anxious. Similarly, he would not be frightened by hearing of a fearful thing that may be far away from him, it must be perceived by his senses before fear and terror can take hold of him.

Many varied things can cause fear in humans such as the fear of a leader or influential person from being dismissed, or the fear of a wealthy man from poverty and similar misfortunes. However, real fear and terror are immediately felt when the individual is threatened by an impending danger that may cause him possibly unbearable pain or death. This is the emotion that scares and agitates and shows itself in the external behavior of the person and his facial features. In addition, the fearful person may be frightened by a sudden quaking such as an earthquake, or a very loud noise such as thunder, or by seeing dead or badly wounded bodies.

However it must be noted that there are differences between people in the way they respond to fearful things. Some are by nature strong in their temperament. Their hearts are not greatly disturbed by sudden or scary encounters. On the other hand, there are those whose disposition is so reactive that they may become stunned and rendered unable to think of any way out of their predicament.[14] In this, they resemble the behavior of most animals such as horses that respond with sudden jerks and darts when fleeing from frightening things that they hear or see. When man behaves in this way tactics of calm thinking or advice cannot help him, for his behavior will be dominated by the instinctive natural response to flee. It is only when he is able to listen and weigh matters sensibly that our mental maneuvers and external means can be helpful.

One of these tactics is for the frightened person to realize that in most cases, the fear created by the expectation of a threatening experience is much greater than the real experience itself, if it actually occurs. This is because most of what man is afraid of is not really harmful as he expects. This is confirmed by the saying that "most of what you fear will not harm you" and the other saying, "most of the

---

[14] In this statement, al-Balkhī speaks about the individual differences in responding to fearful situations in a way very similar to the modern theory of autonomic liability or reactivity propounded by H.J. Eysenck (1997). Eysenck believed that there are individual differences between peoples' autonomic responses to anxiety-provoking stimuli. Those who are very reactive are predisposed to develop anxiety disorders more than those with comparatively less reactive autonomic nervous systems and that this is an inherited trait.

terror comes from the anticipation of the terror". For this reason, some of the scholars have likened the things that frighten people to a thick ground fog in a cold country. An uninformed person (like an Arab Bedouin living in a hot desert) would think it to be a solid (black) object without any outlets and that it can trap people inside it. However if daring to enter he would find it to be simply moist air that he can breathe.

This illustration is analogous to the experience of almost all people. Nobody has not experienced fear and worry about a certain future occurrence only to find, after experiencing it, that their fear was exaggerated and unfounded.[15] They would also discover that the experience they once thought fearful was not really different to other occurrences they dealt with effectively. In learning this lesson, such people often benefit from this understanding in facing future predicaments.

However, wiser people may not even need to experience such personal encounters in order to tranquilize their fear, learning through observation of the behavior of those having successfully dealt with fear-evoking situations similar to ones they expected to face. This kind of thinking would help one avoid being disturbed and defend one's soul from the assault of fear and terror. Such a person must realize that he has a number of mental maneuvers that he can use to heal fear and terror (or at least to reduce their effect), but if he allows himself to succumb to fear and panic, he will not be in a position to benefit from these thought tactics. He should not let himself be overcome by fear to the extent of falling into the trap that he wishes to save himself from.

Another useful tactic is to invoke anger against one's fearful behavior by appealing to one's pride, thus rebuking the soul for being scared and telling oneself that being so terrorized and panicky is not the respected behavior of esteemed men but rather cowards or perhaps those of weak disposition such as women and children. As anger at oneself increases, so self-pride will be enhanced and one will feel

---

[15] It is of interest to note that modern eminent cognitive therapists like Ellis and Beck have considered exaggeration as one of the major forms of faulty thinking that leads to all sorts of anxiety disorders and depression.

ashamed and guilty of behaving like a spineless coward or those of weak disposition. Indeed, there is no way to fight fear and terror that is more effective than arousing pride and self-importance. Pride is the motive that strengthens the hearts of the criminals and victims who bravely and patiently stand the unbearable excruciating punishments executed against them by kings and sultans.

Fear can also be opposed by employing a method of thought in some ways similar to the previous one. One facing a fearful experience should convince himself that those succumbing to such frightening things are simply naive and ignorant people with no past experience in hearing, or seeing frightening occurrences, or knowing how to manage them. It is known that those who repeatedly face terrifying incidents become accustomed to them and their fear is reduced each time the fearful episode is repeated. This is why children and animals become quite scared when they face any new situation or hear loud noises, responding with terror even if these occurrences are not really dreadful. Because of ignorance they exaggerate their responses. Were they to acknowledge that such seemingly fearsome things are in reality harmless, they would respond like mature individuals.

Even if adults were to witness the horrors of war, seeing wounded and dead people for the first time in their lives, they would be greatly frightened. But were they to engage in much combat in an army, they would become used to the scenes of warfare. For this reason, it is customary for kings and governors to send their children at an early age to see the horrors of warfare in order for them to become used to the sight of dead and injured soldiers so that they grow up as brave warriors.

Comparable to this is the behavior of physicians who treat patients with serious injuries and who perform various operations. Once their eyes become accustomed to such scenes, they are not affected by them. On the other hand new medical practitioners and those outside the profession would be greatly terrified by such dreadful sights. A third example is that of seamen and passengers who frequently travel by sea. Because of long experience in stormy seas containing terrifying huge waves, their senses become accustomed and they lose their fear. Likewise in the case of those living in regions of frequent earthquakes.[16] With repeated exposure to such, otherwise panic-provoking, experiences they may not be alarmed or scared, unlike those living in regions of no earthquakes or where the phenomenon is rare. Akin to this is the behavior of a person afflicted with a serious physical illness. When the symptoms first appear, he is overwhelmed with fear and anxiety but as the disorder becomes chronic, he begins to habituate himself to its symptoms until they cause him no more worry.

These examples clearly illustrate the importance of habituation and the familiarity of our senses in tranquilizing fear. They demonstrate that ignorance concerning the real nature of things is behind most human fears and terrors and that educating people regarding what they wrongly fear would help to heal them. This explains why we see an uninformed person scared of what he sees or hears even with respect to natural events whereas the learned remain unmoved because they know the physical reasons for the occurrence. For example, scholars are not roused into fear upon eclipses of the sun or moon, or occurrence of quakes and tremors,[17] and this should remind us of our earlier discussion with regard to the fear responses of children and animals concerning harmless sights and sounds due to their ignorance and unfamiliarity.

Adults in this respect are no different from them. Their dread is not unlike that of horses and other riding animals that are scared of statues or even pictures of lions and other dangerous carnivores, or birds scared of scarecrows. If these animals knew of the harmless nature of these things they would show no fear of them. But we know from our experience that an animal scared of such a harmless thing can be healed if repeatedly brought near to the object until becoming used to it, thereafter passing it by without showing fear or interest. However animals are different from children in this respect. An animal

---

[16] These examples remind one of the work of Wolpe in reciprocal inhibition as well as the modern behavioral therapeutic technique of exposure therapy that was earlier known as flooding.

[17] It seems that al-Balkhī has not had experience with earthquakes or he lived in tents or houses built from light materials that do not cause death and devastation when they collapse as a result of earthquakes. Otherwise, ignorant persons, as well as scholars, should be scared of earthquakes.

that has a natural fear of such harmless things would continue to exhibit this emotion as long as it lives. Children, on the other hand, would lose such infantile dread through the process of maturity and development. It is not within the nature of animals to overcome their ignorance by mere maturity and experience.

From this we conclude that the best methods for tranquilizing fear and panic are to acquire much knowledge and information of fearsome things (to discover that they are not really harmful) and to force oneself to repeatedly expose one's hearing and sight to noxious things, though disliking the practice, until one's senses are familiarized by them. In tolerating the pain of this exercise one is in fact training oneself like the riding animal forced by the whip to move again and again near the thing it is scared of until it becomes used to it and loses its fear.[18]

CHAPTER [7] *Methods of Dealing with Sadness and Depression*

THE SYMPTOMS OF SADNESS and depression are of special significance in comparison to other psychological symptoms since they can cause very severe reactions to man when they take over his heart. This fact is clearly illustrated by the serious changes that afflict an individual suffering from acute sadness and depression. He appears in the most horrible form, uncontrollable deeds demonstrating his impatience and annoyance. In an earlier chapter we stated that depression is an extreme form of grief and sadness. Depression in its acute form is like a blazing coal fire while sadness is analogous to coal that remains glowing after the fire has subsided. These symptoms have pronounced effects in exhausting the body, draining its activity and wearing out its wish for pleasurable desires. It is as if the healthy human soul can almost be considered the sunlight of the body, which

---

[18] There can be no more simplified and clearer statement to show that the best treatment for fear and anxiety is cognitive and behavior therapy by gradual reciprocal inhibition. Indeed, this shows the genius of al-Balkhī in arriving through reason, centuries ago, with therapies close to our modern techniques of cognitive behavior therapy.

can be totally eclipsed by sadness and depression, losing its glowing rays and turning into utter darkness. In sum we say that sadness is the opposite of joyfulness and happiness. The face of a happy elated person radiates with cheeriness and brightness while that of the depressed expresses gloom, pessimism and despair.

Just as fear and anxiety are caused by the expectation of a future threat, sadness and depression are caused by the loss of something the person loves or is attached to. Thus fear is directed to the future and sadness to the past. They are the strongest among psychological symptoms. If they join forces in afflicting a person, he would have the worst kind of an unhappy miserable and dejected life. But if he is saved from them he would enjoy a blissful happy life. However, no one should aspire to rid himself from all sorts of anxiety and sadness since this world is not the place where people can enjoy a life of total freedom from fear and sadness. This condition is only granted to the saved ones in Paradise in the Hereafter. These are the happy people whom Allah has repeatedly described in the Qur'an as the ones who "Shall have no fear nor shall they be sad or grieve".[19] They shall not be fearful about whatever they expect in their future nor sad about what they have left behind in their earthly life. In only these few words, Allah will bring to them all what they wish to have and preclude them from whatever is disliked by them.

However our discussion in this chapter will be on the sadness and depression that people suffer from in this world. Whether slight or severe, to the extent of causing the person to lose his patience, no one can avoid being subjected to these symptoms since this is imbedded in the nature of life in this world. We begin by stating that sadness is of two distinct types.[20] The first type is the one that has a clear identifiable cause such as the death of a beloved relative or the loss of wealth or something that the person greatly values. The second type has no

19 The Qur'an, chapter 2 verse 38.

20 This, as we said, is one of al-Balkhī's most amazing discoveries – that of classifying depression into a comparatively mild reactive mood disorder with known reasons and an indigenous major depression for which there are no clear reasons and which is related to dysfunction in the chemistry of the body (brain). The former responds to psychotherapy; the latter needs physical treatment as well.

obvious cause. It is a sudden distress and gloom that descends over the affected person preventing him, most of the time, from exuberance of activity and the enjoyment of the usual pleasures of this world. The person afflicted is generally unaware of any clear reason for his dejection.

The causes behind the latter type of sadness or depression for which there is no known reason are related to bodily symptoms such as the impurity of the blood, its coolness and the changes in its contents. The treatment for this symptom is physical and psychological. As for the physical, it concentrates on purifying the blood, increasing its temperature and making it lighter. The psychological is limited to gentle encouraging talk that brings back some happiness[21] as well as listening to music and songs[22] and similar activities that emotionally give warmth to the gloomy.

The sadness or depression that has a known reason i.e. loss of a loved relative or inability to obtain something one desperately wants is a symptom that can be helped with mental practices and is the disorder to which we are devoting this chapter. As previously stated, with respect to other symptoms its treatment is based on two strategies: an internal and an external approach. The external, as already mentioned, is carried out by specialized counselors and wise preachers whose job is to raise morale and heal the sadness. This approach, as stated earlier, is analogous to the external treatment of body symptoms by medicines and special drinks. The internal strategies, on the other hand, concern a number of mental mechanisms based on optimistic thought that a person creates within his soul to train himself to overcome any sorrowful feelings that appear due to losing what he prizes or failing to obtain what he desperately desire.

One of the thought mechanisms is to weigh up the excessive bodily harm that continued sadness and depression can cause to one's body with the urge to mourn over his loss. Logical thinking would convince the person in question that his bodily health should be the most

[21] Here al-Balkhī is clearly speaking about a talking cure that was developed about 11 centuries after his death and was given the name "psychotherapy".

[22] Here again is an important contribution of using music therapy and singing to move and bring delight to the endogenously depressed.

beloved thing to him. He should not accept to trade it in for any sum of money or relatives. The fact that a person feels sad and depressed for presumed loss is actually because he loves his body and soul and wants to please himself with what he failed to obtain or to stop the loss from happening. Destroying his health in agony over what has been lost, would be akin to someone selling out his capital to gain some little profit. Pondering on this would prove to the one afflicted that he would be the loser should he allow sadness to subdue his soul and harm his body.

Another maneuver is for one to understand and realize that life in this world, by its very nature, is not the abode of perpetual joy and happiness, nor the abode of avoiding any loss of loved ones or sought after desires. One should look around to see if anyone has been spared such losses and bereavements. None will be found. If this is the way of things then one should deeply convince oneself that all the pleasures one obtains in life are but an additional gift that should be enjoyed with delight and that the losses one suffers and (those things) which one is unable to attain should not cause one much sorrow and bereavement. This should give one a fairly happy life of satisfaction and contentment.[23]

In addition to that, the sad person who behaves with extreme impatience and uncontrolled bereavement when he faces a misfortune should seriously consider this weak behavior as a greater calamity than what he had faced. The reason for this is that life in this world will certainly bring to him more losses and if he is to respond every time with impatience to these future unhappy occurrences, his life would certainly be a very wretched one. Accordingly, a wise person should train himself to face the misfortune or loss with disciplined endurance until this becomes a usual pattern of confronting future mishaps. If this disciplinary training is carried out, one would reduce

---

[23] It is obvious that al-Balkhī got this idea from some of the *aḥādīth* (plural of hadith) of Prophet Muhammad. In one of them the Prophet is quoted to have said, "In matters of this world look around to see those who are less than you or those who suffer more, and in matters of the *akhirah* or Hereafter, look at those who are better than you in their worshipping of Allah. This would cause you not to belittle what Allah has given you in this world and would motivate you to do more for your Hereafter." (Bukhārī)

all misfortunes to only the one that he had overcome: that of losing patience in confronting mishaps.

One more mental tactic, (already mentioned), is for one to become strongly conscious of the fact that those who lose their patience and succumb to despair and helplessness are spineless cowards or the weak. On the other hand, it is those who face calamities and catastrophes with unbending endurance that have been exalted by their societies. Their tales of fortitude and courageous forbearance have been recorded in the history of their nation as exemplary characters to be modeled. One facing a saddening event should ask himself whether he would want to be like the cowards or whether he should model himself after glorified heroes.

A further mental approach is to realize that one's soul or self should be and is in fact the most precious thing that one has and that one should preserve it. If it is safe, then any other loss should comparatively be much less disturbing and tolerable. This being the case, facing any loss that affects one's soul with excessive sorrow and dejection is unjustified.[24] This kind of tranquilizing thought should be linked to the convincing fact that any hardship or damaging loss that besets one is similar or even less severe than the predicaments other people have suffered or are now suffering from. It is one of the characteristics of human nature to find solace in one's hardship when one discovers that it is shared by many other people. Furthermore, one should always remember that incidents that cause people to feel sad or to grieve are part of the engraved nature of this life. This kind of thoughtful tranquility is bound to help one to control distress and mourning and not allow them to multiply in an unchecked manner.

One more mental approach is to ponder on reducing the effect of the calamity that is afflicting one by realizing that it could have been much more depressive and agonizing. Imagining that it could have come in a much more sorrowful and grieving manner may cause one to be grateful to God for saving one from a possibly greater catastrophe and giving one a lighter misfortune. At any rate, since the soul has been spared from demise and there is the future to make up for what

---

[24] In saying this, al-Balkhī seems to be repeating himself.

had been lost, one must reflect on the gifts that God has bestowed on one and to see how best to make use of them. The expectation of such future pleasures can help to soothe the depressive mood and even transform it to one of happiness.

Finally, by surveying one's own as well as other's experiences, one will come to the realization that all incidents of sorrow and grief are destined to be forgotten and that with the passing of days the agony would certainly diminish. One must take cognizance of the fact that the most saddening moment of an incident is its inception and that the days that come after will certainly reduce its painful effects until it is gradually pushed into forgetfulness. This kind of mental maneuver is bound to bring about a quick feeling of comfort or even happiness and pleasure.

We have delineated in this chapter the methods that can be used to overcome sadness and depression caused by distressing life experiences. These are the mental maneuvers that, with the help of Allah, can be very beneficial to those who need to overcome their sorrow and grief.

CHAPTER [8] *Mental Maneuvers that Fend off the Recurring Whispers of the Heart and the Obsessive Inner Speech of the Soul*

WE HAVE ALREADY STATED in an earlier chapter that the obsessive inner speech of the soul is one of the symptoms that can be helped by the psychological healing of the soul. Actually this symptom is one of the most harmful and damaging to man. This is due to the fact that though it is considered a psychological disorder, in reality it is not purely so. Its etiology is shared with organic bodily aspects.[25] No human being is spared from occasional or frequent anxiety, anger and sadness, but this repetitive inner rumination of the soul is not as common. A person may be spared from this symptom throughout his

[25] It is worth noting that modern research subscribes to this perceptive clinical observation of al-Balkhī. Many research studies have indicated that heredity and other neurological etiology are behind the affliction of obsessive-compulsive disorder.

life without ever complaining from its harmful effect. This does not mean that he does not experience an inner self conversation of the soul since this is a common disposition of the human soul that is part of human nature.[26] What we mean is that this monologue does not recur in an obsessive manner that interferes with everyday chores nor does it bring fearful thoughts or make one imagine dejecting things. That is why we say that its etiology has a share with the body.

However it must be stressed that it can also be harmful to the body like physical symptoms or even more so. This is because the pure bodily symptoms are pains and aches (that can be treated by medicines) but the harm done by this psychological symptom is more concealed and varied. Repetitive whispering can have an inherited predisposition or it may appear as an unexpected symptom due to some (negative) experiences. Though the obsessive symptom that originates from an inborn disposition[27] is more frequently suffered from during one's life, it is still less stressful than the one that suddenly afflicts the person at a later age in a way that he has not experienced before. In the first instance, the victim would have already accustomed himself to these intruding thoughts and does not expect his condition to worsen. He may feel better and momentarily forget his problem whenever he is very busy with important issues. In the second case, however, the first unexpected attacks would cause so much tension that he may deteriorate to an unbearable level of anxiety and fretfulness. Conversely, when the disorder is caused by an inherited temperament it usually does not seriously worsen. In fact it may become habitual and the afflicted may only suffer from the symptom when alone or when not engrossed in some demanding business.

The different reactions of the victims to these two types of affliction with this psychological symptom are very much similar to the response of the sick to bodily illnesses. Some illnesses and physical disorders attack the person because of inborn factors in his body or

[26] Notice his clear differentiation between normal and pathological self-talk.

[27] This statement shows the refined clinical observation of al-Balkhī since the role of heredity in obsessive compulsive disorder has now been supported by a number of modern researches.

because of natural predisposition and temperament. Because of the high frequency with which such illness occurs, the afflicted will get used to them. Disorders such as headaches and common pains of the chest, stomach or ear, which are rooted in man's inborn dispositions come and go with or without medicines. Unlike disorders and pains that are tolerated because of the frequency of attacks, illnesses that afflict suddenly, without warning, are quite disturbing to the body.

This symptom of unrelenting whispers and obsessive thoughts is caused by the dominance of black bile in the body. This can happen in one of two ways: firstly by an inborn natural disposition in which the sufferer has inherited a preponderance of black bile in comparison to other humors. This will predispose him to experience bad thoughts and ugly inner speech. The second is caused by a disproportion in his humors. He does not directly inherit a high proportion of black bile, but he inherits a mixture of yellow bile and phlegm. The yellow bile which is dry and warm reacts with the phlegm changing its cool humid nature into dry warm black bile that causes the obsession of thought. However this latter mixture produces less striking symptoms than the former since it is the result of pure unadulterated black bile. Thus the second type is an unnaturally developed black bile but the former is the more powerful natural one.

A person who has a natural predominance of black bile can be identified from the characteristics of his body and his emotional responses. He would have a solid condensed body type with large bones and tense a‘ṣāb (muscles),[28] dried out skin, thick blood, curly short hair and rather dusty grimy skin color. Psychologically he would generally be a dismal, but aggressive person with a constantly annoyed, angry face. He is silent most of the time putting up a serious expression, as if he were contemplating. He is not angered easily, but when really provoked it is very difficult for him to forget or to accept apologies. He would generally continue to show malevolence and hatred even to those who in their apology show him a high degree of warmth and affection.

[28] Al-Balkhī used the Arabic words a‘ṣāb to stand for muscles. Nowadays, this word stands for nerves.

Of course there are people afflicted with obsessions though they do not have the bodily or psychological characteristics that we have just mentioned, such as being in possession of a pliable soft body and behaving in a sociable conversational manner with an effort to please others. Contrary to the first group they are changeable and moody, easily infuriated and quick to forgive. Whenever a person shows these qualities but also suffers from inner whispers and obsessive thoughts, it must be inferred that the black bile in his system is only a result of the mixture of yellow bile and phlegm. In such cases, the harm he gains from this symptom would be less than the previous type in whom the black bile is natural, originating from an inborn temperament. Though the black bile in the second type is developed from the mixture of phlegm and yellow bile, the phlegmatic moisture does not totally lose its influence. It prevents his symptom from becoming too acute and anxiety provoking.

Even if the symptom of the obsession is less pronounced in the second type, the afflicted will continue to suffer much. That is so because this obsessive symptom, unlike the other symptoms that we have discussed, is very difficult to treat or to get rid of.[29] Furthermore, it does not have a straightforward unambiguous cause. In the case of anger and rage or fear and panic, we always know the direct stimulating cause and by manipulating it, we can help the person to overcome it. For example the angry person can lose his fury by avenging himself or by forgetting the incident after the passage of time. Similarly, the frightened, panicky person would revert to tranquility as soon as the fearsome object or occurrence is removed. The same applies to all other emotional symptoms. They come and go and most people are saved from their hurtful effects during most of the days of their lives. For example you will not find a person who is perpetually enraged or frightened. But as for the symptom of this repetitive inner speech or the harmful monologue of the soul, its cause is unknown and it is not easily treated. It is something that befalls an individual as a result of inborn disposition as we have mentioned.

[29] Again this is one of al-Balkhī's wonderful clinical observations. Obsessive-compulsive disorder is indeed the most difficult to treat in comparison to other anxiety based disorders.

This obsessive monologue of the soul is not limited to hateful thoughts. It can obsess with thoughts about something that one loves and deeply wishes to have. So, irresistibly falling in love may at times be seen as such an obsession. Such thoughts about a beloved object may be so overwhelming that the person may be hindered from thinking about anything else concerning his livelihood or even his other pleasures. But of course the really harmful way in which this symptom afflicts is when it possesses the person with threatening and fearful thoughts. Such persistent thoughts would make him imagine that a dreadful incident is going to befall him or that a physical harm is about to badly affect his body. The latter obsessive thought is much more disturbing since one's body is the most precious thing to a person. So, repetitive notions that overawe one with fearful or worrying thought cause much more anxiety and concern than ones that overpower the mind with what a person loves or greatly wishes to possess. The latter is always associated with some of the imagined pleasure of realizing one's desires.

It must be stated that recurring negative thoughts of the fearful and worrying type can also be harmful to the body. This is because as the symptom intensifies, the sickened soul would give the person afflicted a strong feeling of the distant event, in space and time, being imminent or about to happen.[30] When this sad state takes its toll, the person would find himself unable to use his mental faculties to deal with anything else, and would be too busy with the imagined imminent danger to enjoy any pleasures or to concentrate on what is said to him or to socialize with others. Whenever he tries to let go and socialize, the disturbing thoughts will shoot up to control his mind. This would leave him a victim of his own negative dreadful thinking and agitating inner talk.

This miserable condition is comparable to one who is continuously subjected to horrible nightmares from which he awakens in a terrible

---

[30] Compare this with Beck's cognitive assumptions about the thinking disorder in anxiety neurosis in which the patient has repetitive thoughts about a far-fetched danger. This is what he calls, "false alarms" development of dysfunctional thought and his theory of maximization and minimization.

state of fear and anxiety. These recurring frightening dreams occur to some people during the night while the nightmarish thoughts of the one afflicted with this symptom of obsessive self-talk possess him during the day. The sufferer imagines impending danger and threatening occurrences in his wakeful inner whispers, while the dreamer sees these frightening incidents in his sleep; however they are both caused by internal self-talk.

An additional distinctive attribute of those suffering from this symptom is their extreme pessimism, they harbor negative thoughts not only about themselves, but also about their surroundings. They worry and feel anxious about trivial things that are not supposed to cause such negative responses, and they always expect the worst and most terrifying outcome to occur. In whatever is expected to happen in their lives they suppress the optimistic and constructive aspects and choose to worry about harmful and negative expectations. This includes whatever happens to their bodies or their surroundings, always mulling over anxiety-provoking imaginary incidents.

It is therefore essential that a person afflicted by, or tested with, this symptom, does his utmost best to find ways of healing himself by all possible means from its harmful effects. In this he should be as highly motivated as one who seeks medicines to relieve painful bodily ailments. He should not be misled by the erroneous belief that a psychological symptom of this nature is untreatable usually afflicting certain people who then have to live with it. On the contrary, he should strongly hold on to the conviction that Allah has not created a disease of the body or a disorder of the soul without creating its antidote. Thus whenever a disease or disorder, whether physical or psychological, is treated with its suitable antidote, it will either be totally cured or at least it's painful or negative effects will be reduced. Even in the latter case one should accept the fact that reducing the severity of a symptom is much better than leaving it untreated until it worsens and causes much more harm.

As we have stated earlier, bodily physical symptoms should naturally be treated by physical therapies (such as medicines or diet); similarly, psychological symptoms should logically be aided by psychological therapies. Such psychological therapies, as stated earlier, are either of an external nature, such as preaching and counseling, or internal, such as in the form of thoughts a person can generate to defend himself against fear, anxiety or sadness if internal whispering creates such negative emotions. It is our obligation (in this chapter) to describe all the mental strategies that can be used to heal this symptom or reduce its harmful effect.

These mental maneuvers, as expected, come either from outside the soul or within it. Externally, it is very important for the one afflicted to avoid being alone since loneliness would naturally stimulate negative thought and harmful self-talk. The human soul is perpetually active either externally or internally.[31] Externally its activity is to busy itself with socializing with other people, talking to them and arguing with them about things that concern the person. Internally, it is to busy itself with thinking, memories and reflections.[32] So if the soul is not occupied by outward conversation, it has no alternative but to be employed in inner thought and past reflections. Such thoughts and whispering self-talk will be particularly intense when the soul is by its nature sensitive and imaginative. Thus a person suffering from this obsessive symptom, will find its harmful effects multiplied when he is alone. But when in the company of other people, actively engaged in amusing conversation and discussion, he will find the influence of inner whispering much reduced. For this reason, being alone and solitude are inadvisable and disapproved of, while mixing with people is commendable.

---

[31] Advising the obsessive-compulsive patient to avoid being alone is a very useful therapeutic technique that I do not find in modern books in psychotherapy or psychiatry. This may be due to the fact that in modern western life it is difficult for relatives and friends to spend much time with such patients. Time is money and no one wishes to throw away money for an obsessive patient.

[32] The fact that the human psyche, supported by the nervous system, is "uninterruptedly active" is beautifully described by Ibn Qayyim al-Jawziyyah in his book *Al-Fawā'id*. He says that the human soul is as active as a continuously revolving millstone. It never stops day or night. The thoughts and feelings are like the seeds that the mill grinds. If you put valuable healthy thoughts into it, it is as if you feed it with wheat. It will come out as flour, but if you put gravel and stones, it will grind it as well, but what are you going to get at the other end?

This is generally true. However, being alone can be advisable for certain special groups of people, such as rulers of a state, concerned with drafting well thought out acts and measures for the running of their country, or for wise scholars, in a library trying to come up with a novel discipline or writing a new book, or the devoted worshipper who loves to be alone with his Lord in spiritual consciousness. Other than such endeavors, loneliness is blameworthy since it can only lead to useless and aimless thinking.

Allah has created man a social being who instinctively enjoys mixing with other people of his resemblance and who needs the social support of others when suffering any sad experiences. Consequently it can be safely said that those who voluntarily prefer to avoid socializing with others without one of the three legitimate reasons that we have specified, must be considered abnormal and lacking in humanity by failing to gain pleasure and benefit from what has been placed into the natural human disposition. This inherited tendency towards companionship can even be observed in certain animals, especially tame ones such as sheep, cattle and birds that flock together. It is wild and aggressive animals such as lions and tigers that favor loneliness.

The benefits of social interaction between humans, whether they are living in their towns or traveling, is so highly considered that it has become a well-known Arabic saying that, "the lone person is a devil". Numerous tales in the literature recount stories of those who traveled alone going through unfamiliar harsh terrain without companions only to end up suffering unendurable catastrophes, untimely death or aimless wandering and mental illness. This is why we place emphasis on the person being tested with obsessive self-talking whispers to avoid being alone.

A second advice for persons afflicted is to avoid idleness and unemployment, since this is the other side of the loneliness coin and can have the same harmful effects of instigating negative persistent thought. If one does not take up an activity that externally consumes one's time, one's soul will naturally turn to internal activity, which would obviously lead to harmful whispers. It is thus highly recommended for such psychological sufferers to develop much interest in jobs that consume their spare time. If they are among the commoners, they can busy themselves with securing earnings for their daily living, but if they are rulers and kings, then they should use their time in improving the wellbeing of their subjects and followers.

However, if the person feels bored (after long hours of concentrated work), he can refresh himself with enjoyable pleasures such as food and drink, sexual relations, listening to moving songs and music, and looking at a delightful landscape and beautiful objects. Such moments of enjoyment would no doubt distract him away from the repetitive whispering of obsessive thoughts. However, it is important for such persons not to make a routine out of any recreational activity. They must be renewed whenever possible in order to keep up the level of enjoyment. This is so because such afflicted persons, (in comparison to normal people), are very quick to become bored by repetitive activities. Even if the moment had been a pleasurable one, its repetition may soon cause the soul to become bored leading it to quickly return to its harmful thoughts. Any novel pleasurable experience will have an effect for some time, thus the afflicted person may need these constant changes so long as his suffering continues.

An additional mental tactic is for the afflicted person to choose some sincere and trusted relatives or friends, who really love him and wish for his good health and happiness, in order to frankly discuss his problem with them and listen to their counsel and advice. They will expose to him the erroneous nature and irrationality of his negative self-talk. This can be very valuable in restraining the sufferer's pessimistic thoughts.33 It would be as beneficial to him in suppressing harmful thoughts as the optimistic supportive words of a good physician to a patient suffering some physical illness. What we have just described are examples of external maneuvers that a person afflicted can use to overcome the problem of repetitive negative thought.

33 This is exactly what modern psychologists say concerning the use of cognitive therapy in helping obsessive-compulsive patients. Notice that in telling the patient to choose trustworthy loving friends, al-Balkhī is actually talking about the positive qualities of a counselor as we see them today.

We next turn to internal strategies to fight this symptom. In short this is a collection of counteracting arguments that an afflicted person can employ to neutralize or even cancel out the negative whispers of his consciousness whenever they emerge. In doing so he would be in many ways similar to someone arguing in a court of law against the allegations raised by an opponent, falsifying the claims and rendering them invalid and illogical. So, in employing counter thoughts against his inner negative self-talk, the person would be equivalent to a defendant in court arguing against his own self.34

Internal thoughts are of two different types. The first is a collection of healthy thoughts that the person accumulates and stores in memory when in a healthy and relaxed state.35 They are retrieved from memory whenever the negative thoughts emerge. The second category consists of thinking that the person generates when the negative thoughts actually begin their assault with minor doses. This is analogous to an early attack of a physical illness. If left untreated by suitable medicine it may develop into an incapacitating disease. Similarly a thought antidote at the early stages of a psychological disorder of the soul may prevent or greatly reduce the effect of a future psychological catastrophe in which the distressed person may be powerless in the face of exaggerated negative thoughts involving far-fetched calamities, imagined destruction and implausible uncontrollable epidemics.

Such unfounded, imaginary, catastrophic thoughts are of course invalidated by the testimony of all wise people. No one would accept to be a slave of negative whispering self-talk which dominates the soul and messes up one's life. The origin of this obsessive disorder is either the dominance of certain body humors, (as detailed earlier), or from the devil appointed to a person (the *qarīn*) that strives to spoil one's life in this world and the Hereafter.36 The source of the disorder is really not very important. Whether it is the influence of body

---

34 One cannot think of a better example to explain what rational cognitive therapy is all about.

35 Remember his analogy of the first aid kit that he gave in an earlier chapter.

36 This is one of the very few unambiguous references to the religious belief about the role of evil spirits in the causation of psychological disorders in the manuscript.

chemicals or the work of Satan, the person should not succumb to such unfounded thoughts and should fight them with the mental strategies that we have described.

One more mental tactic is for the person afflicted to observe the way people around him react to his terrifying or sad inner whispers which are causing him to demoralize himself or destabilize the way he lives. He should reason with himself that if his harmful whispers and self-talk had any reality then surely people around him would have been disturbed. And since as clearly apparent they are not, for people in general will only be alarmed by real threatening dangers they can actually perceive, then it must follow that this negative thought must be unreal, just like the delusions of the mentally disturbed. This can be a useful thought against the obsessive symptom.

An additional useful thought is to deliberate on the problem and its causes. Doing so, the sufferer would come to the conclusion that his symptom, despite its persistent pains and worries, was actually rooted in his natural disposition and temperament. He should then convince himself that any predisposed psychological disorder should not cause him to be disturbed or scared since he knows of its origin, and accordingly expects its occurrence. In this he should be like the one suffering from a chronic physical bodily complaint. Such a person quickly learns to live with it and familiarizes himself with its pains. In fact there are very few people indeed who do not complain of a physical disorder that afflicts them because of their natural predisposition and inherited temperament. The fact that these physical symptoms continue for a long time would help them to accustom themselves to them. Also, such a person will come to realize that his negative whispers would not endanger his life or cause him to suffer incapacitating disease allowing him to tolerate and live happily with them. The fact that they are afflicting him because of his inherited predisposition, his inability to change, would further support him in tolerating them.

In a way this is similar to the behavior of one who suffers from frequent nightmares. On first experiencing them, he would respond with terror and anxiety, but upon continuously seeing them in his sleep, he will gradually become accustomed to them and they would cease to frighten him, particularly when he realizes that his vulnerability to such scary dreams is the result of his disposition and temperament. Such thoughts should be employed by one who suffers from harmful obsessive whispering in order to counteract the symptom.

Another very important approach is for one to deliberate on the fact that Allah (SWT), Blessed and Elevated be His Name, has created highly fixed laws for the development and growth or weakening and decaying for all sorts of plants, animals and even non-living things. Nothing will flourish and develop without specific reasons that precede this, or decay and perish without causes that lead to this. These are the general laws of cause and effect that Allah has set to run our universe. They are confirmed by our everyday observations. These are unchanging laws that govern the life of animals and plants and the existence of inanimate things. For example, we will never see a well-built structure that suddenly collapses without observing agents that cause its walls to develop fissures and cracks or seeing persons who deliberately use tools to tear it down. Similarly, we cannot expect an oil lamp to abruptly be extinguished if all the essential constituents for its continued illumination are at hand. If it has a good wick and the correct amount of oil that does not flood it with abundance nor cause it to burst into flames due to its shortage, it must continue to give light unless someone extinguishes it by pouring water over the burning wick or it is extinguished by a sudden gust of air.

Likewise, the life of a healthy person is not expected to suddenly be terminated without an observable external or internal agent that causes its death. This, of course, does not exclude disease and the gradual decline caused by old age that naturally leads to demise. In using the analogy of the oil lamp, the wick stands for the human body, the oil for its nourishment, and the lamp with its light to life itself. The agents that extinguish the light of the wick are like the adverse surroundings that are being subjected to very high or very cold temperatures, beating, punching, knocking, wounding, or similar hazardous accidents. Accordingly, if the person leads a safe life that precludes such precarious incidents, consumes good nourishing food and drink, and takes part in other relevant activities that enhance his health, there would be no reason for him to accept any negative thoughts with regards to his sudden demise in the same way that no one should expect the light of an oil lamp to be extinguished, if there is no external agent that interferes to put out its flame. Such thoughts would no doubt be helpful to the one obsessed in counteracting negative self-talk concerning his health and supposed imminent death.

A further thought tactic is to ponder on the fact that anything that is created on the basis of causes and their effects has certain factors by which we can judge its resilience or weakness against the adverse agents that face it. We can judge its expected age and the speed with which eradicating agents succeed in destroying it. For example if we see a strongly constructed edifice built with thick walls from pure unadulterated material, we would conclude that the agents of diminution cannot easily weaken its walls and that it will continue standing for a very long time unless it is subjected to the interference of an external demolisher. Similarly, the healthy life of a human being and his expected age can be judged from certain bodily or psychological characteristics or from his own self.

The physical features that can predict one's anticipated age can be accurately determined by the physician. For instance, if he finds that the person concerned has a weak digestive system and is chronically complaining from various ailments that come and go, he would deduce that he will not have a long life but, in contrast, if he finds the person well-built with a healthy digestive system he would conclude that he will have a long life.

As for the prediction of one's age from estimates not depending on physical or psychological characteristics, one would cite the work of fortune-tellers and astrologers. They foretell the expected ages of newly born infants to kings and rulers. Though they may wrongly guess in minor cases, they are not likely to commit such mistakes in major issues. This (psychic science) should not be taken lightly. It is a valuable profession of great importance.[37] Though it has been practiced by experts from far-flung countries, they all seem to agree on its interpretations, its general rules of applications and its divisions and

---

37 It is rather strange that al-Balkhī in the 3rd century after Hijra would support the practice of fortune telling though the position of Islam is quite clear about refuting it.

branches. The possibility of communication between these experts in plotting to create such a profession is indeed a very remote possibility. Their interpretations are either based on religiously revealed knowledge that would definitely tell the truth, or from their own ideas that can lie, or from common sense and reasoning on which people would not agree on an irrational verdict.

Now, if our description of this profession is accurate, then its judgments as to one's age, fortune, happiness or other aspects should be taken seriously and optimistically. If this optimism entailed by the absence of a forecast of bad luck or misfortune is coupled with a healthy strong body that is free from chronic complaints and is able to reasonably gratify the needs of food, drink and sex and living without serious psychological problems, then succumbing to harmful whispers and negative self-talk becomes a pointless inconceivable form of behavior. This approach in thinking should be intelligently used by the one afflicted with the obsessive symptom to fight his harmful inner whispers.

As we have already mentioned, sufferers from obsessive inner whisperings are highly pessimistic people. They demean themselves and exaggerate minor complaints and amplify trivial misfortunes to look as if they were incapacitating catastrophes. Another way that helps in remedying this condition is for the obsessed person to contemplate the powerful grip that Allah has given to nature and how He has fixed the exact age of every living person. Our Creator, the Most High and Blessed, has blended human souls into their bodies in the most wonderful and faultless manner, perfectly bonding them in the strongest possible way so that they live together in the most congruous and intimate manner. For this reason you find that the human soul would tolerate all sorts of unimaginable pains, gushing wounds, broken bones, amputations and other mishaps without trying to break off from its body. It can also stand hunger, thirst and chronic serious illnesses that affect the mental faculties and senses and prevent the body it inhabited from taking the food that it badly needs. The soul can endure all that because of the familiarity of its attachment to the body. Not only that but it urgently strives to ward off all the illnesses and dangers that threaten the safety of the body.

In fact if one studies the effect of medicines and the physical therapies of physicians in curing illnesses and diseases, one would find that only very few persons really benefit from such physical therapies. Most will benefit more from the encouragement and (psychological) assistance of the physician. This will enhance the natural power of the soul to heal the body.[38] The evidence for what we have said comes from the behavior of many very sick people who avoid seeking the help of physicians and enjoy all sorts of food and drink (that doctors generally consider as harmful to them), yet they achieve full remission from their disorders. They may lead a healthy life until they reach old age or die because of an epidemic or other unexpected lethal cause. This is indeed clear evidence for the healing power of nature and the supportive influence of the combined sway of body and soul. The lesson to draw from what has been said is that one afflicted with any bodily illness should avoid pessimistic feelings exaggerating the illness into a terminal disease or a destructive catastrophe. Of course this is particularly so with one afflicted with obsessive negative thought.

An extra thought strategy to fight obsessive negative thought is to reflect on the fact that when Allah (Most High and Most Blessed) planned for humans to inhabit the earth, He decreed in His wisdom to make the channels for safe life much greater than the ways and means to unsafe and dangerous existence. This is obvious, since if it were not so, the life of the common people would have been hazardous and disorganized. It is also quite clear from observation that those people who are bodily and psychologically healthy are much more numerous than those who are psychologically disordered or those who are physically disabled such as the blind, the deaf, the dumb or the physically impaired. Likewise, you find the number of the pitiable poor who do not have what they need for mere survival to be very small in comparison to those who can easily pay for their sustenance.

---

[38] Al-Balkhī here is saying exactly what Herbert Benson states in his well-researched book, *Timeless Healing* (Simon & Schuster, 1996). He writes in p.109, "Medicine still offered more care than it did cures, more attention than technology". He goes on to say that successful treatment depends on, "...three modes of belief-inspired healing: the belief of an individual in a treatment, the belief of the caregiver or their mutual beliefs".

Correspondingly, you can observe that those who become extremely sick and die are far less than those who recover from their illnesses and lead a healthy life thereafter. An exception to that, of course, is when there is an epidemic; however such epidemics cannot be taken as an evaluation since they rarely happen. They are the exception not the norm. As a consequence to what we have delineated, the young individual who has not reached the weakness of old age should not entertain pessimistic ideas about his condition when he becomes sick. He should perceive his illness within the general norms of safety that we have discussed. This thought tactic can be of special value to those whose obsessive negative thought leads them to unfounded pessimism.

Another approach of healthy thinking is to mull over the fact that Allah Most High has created man in a way that would not entirely save him from all sorts of physical or psychological maladies. However, He has also created, out of His mercy and compassion, an antidote for each one of these disorders. But He has spread out these antidotes and curing agents in all kinds of plants and animal parts as well as what He has created on top of the earth and under its surface. Not only that, but He has subjugated some of His servants to look for these medicines and bring them to the traders and merchants from far-flung places; from land and sea, from the shores of rivers, the tops of mountains, deep valleys and bottomless oceans.

Furthermore, He has designated some of His slaves to specialize in the profession of medicine that can utilize these therapeutic materials in helping the sick. There should be no doubt in the mind of any astute observer that the origin of this medical profession is a heavenly Divine revelation or at least it is an inspiration that is comparable to Godly revelation. By this Divine inspiration, these physicians were given the intelligent ability of combining the ingredients of these therapeutic potions into predetermined weights, precise quantities or fixed volumes. They must also be revered for documenting their medical knowledge in books that continue to serve future generations.

Accordingly the great services of both the ones who bring the medicinal plants, the therapeutic animal parts or minerals from every corner of the earth, as well as the physicians who astutely combine them to treat the sick, must be appreciated and not be considered as meaningless or fruitless. In fact the fruits of these professions are a gift provided by Allah, Most High and Gracious, to promote the health of His slaves and creatures with the inspiration and support He has bestowed on these qualified experts. Thus, for every kind of disease, illness or disorder, there must be an antidote that would cure it if given in the correct manner.

The antidote in this respect is just like food to the hungry or water to the thirsty. This is so because the One who created the food and water is the same God who created the medicines and antidotes. Both are agents for human wellbeing and safety. And just as food would satisfy the hungry and water the thirsty so that they become satiated, suitable medicine is bound to bring about healing and the patient will regain his health and will no longer need to take the medicine.

However, for the medical ingredients to bring about healing the person must not be too old to benefit from it. Also, he must not be subjected to a contagious epidemic. Moreover, the medicine may not help him if he is careless and follows a happy-go-lucky approach to his eating and drinking habits. If he does not care about what he eats, at what times and in what quantity, he would definitely subject his body to the buildup of harmful waste that can culminate in serious diseases. Similarly, carelessness in seeking medical help when a malady first appears may lead to the worsening of the symptoms until they reach a level that cannot be helped by therapy. And finally, the afflicted person may harm himself by his lack of self-control in taking or doing what the physician has prevented him from. In eating what harms him, he would be like the one who cooperates with the disorder against his natural disposition to improve and against the efforts of his physician.39

On the other hand, the sick person can be much helped by the medicine if he during his healthy life he was careful enough not to

39 In this final section of the book it seems that al-Balkhī has been carried away from his main topic of obsessive disorders to remotely related medical issues. Also his Arabic language becomes more difficult, and he tends to move abruptly from one subject to another. The translator did his best to simplify the material and to rearrange it into a logical sequence.

allow his body to accumulate heavy and sticky harmful waste. But if he develops a little of this refuse and becomes ill, he (should) immediately seek the help of a physician before the malady worsens. This would quickly result in attaining recovery. This recovery would of course be enhanced if the instructions of the physician are meticulously followed. Such a careful person can enjoy good health unless he reaches old age or is harmed by an external causal injury.

These then are the thought tactics (as discussed in this chapter) that a person afflicted with obsessive negative whispering of the soul can employ. With the support of Allah Most High, he would completely neutralize these thoughts or at least reduce their harmful effects.

By the conclusion of this section (on the sustenance of the soul), the whole book is now completed. It is with the support and grace of Allah that this effort has been achieved. May all thanks be to Him and may His prayers and peace be (showered) on our master Muhammad, His illiterate Prophet, and his family and Companions, and may honor and reverence be the attributes of the selected ones among his followers. The close of this book was at the hands of the humble servant of Allah, Shams al-Dīn al-Qudsī, who strives for the forgiveness of his gracious Lord from his sins and who prays that Allah bestows his Prophet Muhammad, who was sent with the perfect infallible message of Islam, with his prayers and salaams.

The (calligraphy) of the book was accomplished on the 18th of the blessed month of Shaʿban in the year 884 after Hijra.[40]

40 The date of the completion of writing the manuscript by the calligrapher, Shams al-Dīn al-Qudsī, is equivalent to Thursday, November 4, 1479 CE. So, the calligrapher rewrote the manuscript six centuries after it was originally authored by al-Balkhī.